CMII

for

Business Process Infrastructure

Vincent C Guess

Holly Publishing
www.hollypublishing.com

Copyright © 2002 by Vincent C Guess
All rights reserved

 Holly Publishing, PO Box 4333
Scottsdale, AZ 85261-4333

Printed in the United States of America

CMII for Business Process Infrastructure / Vincent C Guess

First printing: April 2002
10 9 8 7 6 5 4 3 2 1

ISBN 0-9720582-0-6

Library of Congress Control Number: 2002105621

Key words:
  1. Project Management   2. Quality Assurance
  3. Configuration Management.   4. Change Management.
  4. Requirements Management   6. Data Management
  7. Records Management   8. Document Control
  9. Library Management   I. Title

CMII Bullets (Things that work)

— Leadership with a Vision

— Honesty, Integrity and Fairness as Core Values

— Organize around Core Business Processes

— All Activities Are Requirements-Driven

— Empower Employees as Creators and Users

— Positive Control of Each Step

— Change Faster

— Document Better

— Keep it Simple

— Smile

Introduction

All organizations strive to improve their existing processes in order to be more competitive. Corporate libraries are continually updated with the latest books on best business practices. Professional societies are continually updating their handbooks and books of knowledge.

Organizational leaders routinely search through that ever-growing mountain of information to find any new nuggets of wisdom. That is what we were doing. We were looking for solutions to problems that would not go away. We were operating in what is now known as the "corrective action mode." We could not seem to escape that mode.

We were ready to try any new ideas that came along. Our management was motivated and innovative but our advancements were slow. As we continued to look for the big step, it became increasingly apparent that key building blocks were missing. We proceeded to focus on the underlying infrastructure. By the end of the 1970s, we had escaped the corrective action mode (as described in Chapter 1). That was only the start. Many nuggets of wisdom have been added since and are now referred to as the "CMII principles."

The Institute of Configuration Management was created to carry this effort forward. Our CMII certification program has provided the perfect environment. Our instructors are highly experienced in the field and thoroughly versed in the CMII principles. Our students are from various industries and government agencies. They are also on the leading edge of implementation within their respective environments.

Consequently, we have expert instructors teaching the experts in the field and the experts in the field providing feedback to the instructors. The developers of enabling software tools are also playing an important role in this effort. The give-and-take in the classroom can be very dynamic. Course materials are continually updated accordingly. The result is continuous improvement at its best.

The purpose of this book is to describe the golden nuggets of wisdom we had to discover on our own. We found key elements of those nuggets in a place where no one else was looking and in a specific area of activity where top management is traditionally reluctant to be seen. That area of activity is known as "configuration management." We found the key elements in the military standards that commercially oriented firms wanted no part of.

Those key elements were of limited value in their existing state. We kept the parts we liked and threw out those that had no value. We proceeded to refine the good parts and integrate them into our overall process. One step led to another. By the end of the 1970s, we had a showcase process.

The purpose of this book is to provide organizational leaders with the insight that is needed to transition out of the corrective action mode and into the continuous improvement mode. This book is not intended to provide all the how-to's; those who read this book will understand where they need to focus their process improvement efforts.

Books such as this are normally written in the format of a college text book and are technical in nature. This book is management-oriented and written in the format of a business book to make it easier to read and understand. Configuration management is a complex subject but the complexity is in its administrative, rather than its technical aspects.

The goal of this book is to make the subject matter as clear as possible and do so with the least number of pages. To improve upon this book would be to improve the clarity of the principles and their application and in even fewer pages. That is what CMII is all about.

This book gives organizational leaders a jump start to get where they need to go. Reading this book does not mean they can stop searching through the evolving mountain of books and publications for new nuggets of wisdom. Some of those searches, however, can be redirected toward validation of the principles contained herein.

Acknowledgments

To Curtis Grace — high school ag teacher who entered his "Future Farmer of America" students in parliamentary procedure contests and later stopped by dad's corn field and told me to "get off that tractor and go to college."

To Gene Shelton — my first boss after engineering school who looked at my first project report and directed me to "write it again using half as many words" and, having done so, insisted that I do it again.

To Dorothy Walderman — typist for my fellow project engineers who confided that she preferred to type my project reports because they were the only ones she could understand.

To Brian Gallagher and Roland Paquette — general managers who had the vision and courage to turn us loose and who supported our efforts to implement business process improvements that later became known as CMII.

To Bill Gaw, Bob Keavney, Wade Krauss, Buzz Miller, Frank Rugnetta and Ray Steinway — members of our cross-functional team that achieved overall process improvements that were years ahead of their time.

To Harry Todd, Bill McElroy and Bud Wetzler — who empowered a similar team to implement similar practices in an environment that was entrenched in aerospace paradigms.

To Lloyd Shoppa — who paved the way in this uncharted territory and shared his company's successful solutions with those of us who followed.

To David Echols — who led 50 major universities receiving IBM-donated tools to include CMII in their industrial technology courses, thereby optimizing the potential that those tools would be successful.

To Phil Wolfe and John Riblett — university leaders who understood the value of CM and chose to sponsor our CMII certification program.

To Marlene Whiteside and my daughter Angie — who handled registration and helped cover all the bases during the start-up years.

To the employees of ICM and the exclusive club of CM professionals and CMII-certified graduates — whose combined efforts have brought CMII to critical mass wherein it is being adopted worldwide as best industry practice.

Forward

The competitive strength of an organization is less in what they do than how they do it. It is in their ability to do the right things right. It is in their ability to shift with changing customer demands while continuing to do the right things reliably and efficiently.

How an organization does what it does has everything to do with "process," but that is an oversimplification. A business enterprise has many processes which have many interdependencies. Some are defined and some are not. Some have checks and balances, others do not. Manual intervention is used to bridge the gaps. No single individual understands all of the processes and their interdependencies. The need for improvement is obvious but where to start is a never-ending debate.

The need for improvement is revealed in the form of corrective action. This book explains what it means to operate in the corrective action mode (as most organizations do). They differ only by degree. This book takes you into the downstream trenches where corrective action runs rampant and brings you face-to-face with the problems. It takes you past the symptoms to the underlying causes. Once the root causes are clearly identified, the needed solutions become obvious.

Corrective action does not just happen, it is caused. No organization is immune. It can be measured. Organizations are suffocating on corrective action to the degree that they use intervention resources to rescue schedule and quality. To eliminate the need for corrective action is to eliminate its causes. To eliminate the causes is to fix the processes and that begins with fixing the business process infrastructure.

This book describes the appropriate business process infrastructure that is missing in most organizations. It is a prerequisite for transitioning out of the corrective action mode and into the continuous improvement mode. It provides the foundation upon which projects can be managed and quality can be assured.

Contents
(High Level)

Introduction vii
Acknowledgments ix
Foreword xi
Contents (by Chapter and Sub-Topic) xiii

1 A Little History and Lessons Learned 1

2 CM Paradigms and CMII Principles 11

3 Proof That CM Is, or Is Not, Working 23

4 CM Subprocesses and Terminologies 35

5 The CMII Model 47

6 Product Structuring and Baselines 57

7 Changes, Forms and Effectivities 69

8 Naming and Numbering Conventions 79

9 Data Integrity 89

10 The "V" Model for Development 99

11 Work Centers and Process Standards 111

12 CMII-Compliant Enabling Tools 121

13 CMII Implementation and ROI 131

14 How to Get Started 143

Source for CMII Training 153
Lists of Figures and Tables 154
Glossary of Acronyms and Terms 156
Index 161

Contents
(by Chapter and Sub-Topic)

1 A Little History and Lessons Learned   **1**
The Environment We Were Trying to Automate 2
Upstream Processes and Downstream Problems 3
Concurrent Engineering and Cross-Functional Teams . 4
Build-To-Order With Concurrent Customization . . . 5
Reduced Lead Times Through Capacity Planning . . . 6
Build-To-Print Versus Process Plans 7
Documents and Number of Signatures 8
Best Practice Built on Refined CM Principles 9
Chapter 1 — Summary 10

2 CM Paradigms and CMII Principles   **11**
Configuration Management as Traditionally Defined . 12
CM: A Process for Communicating Formally 13
Standardized Acronyms and Terminologies 14
Contradicting Definitions of Quality 15
Requirements Must Lead, Products Must Conform . . 16
Stove-Pipe Processes and Stand-Alone Systems 17
Fixed Baselines Versus Moving Baselines 18
One Standardized, Enterprise-Wide Change Process . . 19
Potential Conflicts With Cost Accounting 20
CM Reinvented 21
Chapter 2 — Summary 22

3 Proof That CM Is, or Is Not, Working   **23**
Sorting Symptoms From Root Causes 24
Software Development: Statistics for 1995 25
Motor Vehicle Computer System Fiasco 26
FBI's Fiasco With Records 27
Air Traffic Control System Fiasco 28

Random Failures or Is Something Terribly Wrong? . . 29
Safety as Vehicle for Transforming a Company 30
An Organization Serious About Bug-Free Software . . 31
Pay a Little Now or Much More Later 32
Software Process Improvement Statistics 33
Chapter 3 — Summary 34

4 CM Subprocesses and Terminologies   35
Project Management: Two Cycles, not One 36
Quality: Change Definition or Fix Problem 37
Language of CMII: Lowest Common Denominators . 38
Requirements Management 39
Change Management 40
Release Management 41
Data Management 42
Records Management 43
Document Control 44
Library Management 45
Chapter 4 — Summary 46

5 The CMII Model   47
Business of Running a Business 48
What it Means to Be Requirements-Driven 49
Scope and Emphasis of CMII 50
Corrective Action Versus Continuous Improvement . . 51
Prerequisites for Eliminating Corrective Action 52
Intervention Resources and Their Magnitude 53
CMII and the Functional Activities Involved 54
Functional Schematic of the CMII Model 55
Chapter 5 — Summary 56

6 Product Structuring and Baselines   57
Bills of Material and Parent-To-Child Relationships . . 58
System Schematics and Interface Definition 59
End-Item Application Requirements 60

Document Types and User-Friendly Formats 61

Primary Versus Secondary Items and Documents . . . 62

As-Planned and As-Released Baselines 63

Enhanced Approach to Concurrent Engineering . . . 64

Fallacies of Learning Curves 65

Information Repositories 66

Baseline for the Business Enterprise 67

Chapter 6 — Summary 68

7   Changes, Forms and Effectivities   69

Relationships of Lowest Common Denominators . . . 70

Rules of Interchangeability 71

Traceability of Changes to Specific End-Items 72

Lot Traceability 73

Change Forms and Formats 74

Form for Deviations and Waivers 75

Change Effectivities and Controlling Documents . . . 76

Reschedules and Effectivity Maintenance 77

Chapter 7 — Summary 78

8   Naming and Numbering Conventions   79

ID Numbers for Positive Control of Applications . . . 80

Item Identification Numbers: Length and Format . . . 81

Pros and Cons of Significant Numbers 82

Naming Conventions for Physical Items 83

Equivalent and Alternate Item Files 84

Superseded and Superseding Item History File 85

Model Numbers 86

Conventions for Identifying Software 87

Chapter 8 — Summary 88

9   Data Integrity   89

Dependent Demand and Netted Requirements 90

How Data Integrity Influences Performance 91

Example of Data Sets Used In-Series 92

Inaccurate Data: Root Causes Are Interdependent . . 93
Data Integrity Must Be a Quality Initiative 94
Harnessing the Power of Creators and Users 95
Requirements Do Not Have to Be Perfect 96
Regulated Versus Non-Regulated Industries 97
Chapter 9 — Summary 98

10 The "V" Model for Development   99
Development: Three Phases With Eight Steps 100
Design Basis Documents: Four Types 101
Design Basis Extended Into Detailed Designs 102
Planned Versus Evolutionary Development 103
Too Little CM Versus Too Much CM 104
Rescue of Software Documentation and Code 105
Rescue Steps Relative to CMII 108
Legal View of CM and a Producer's Liabilities . . . 109
Chapter 10 — Summary 110

11 Work Centers and Process Standards   111
Work Center Networks and Goals 112
Change Process: A Classic Work Center Network . . 113
Design and Build Standards 114
Identify and Schedule Work Center Tasks 115
Input Validation and Output Verification 116
Time Standards and Consolidation of Work 117
Just-In-Time Principles for Documents 118
Measurement of Process Maturity 119
Chapter 11 — Summary 120

12 CMII-Compliant Enabling Tools   121
Paperless Environment: Finally a Reality 122
Out-Of-The-Box Solution: Not There Yet 123
First Priority: As-Planned and As-Released Baselines 124
Automation of the Closed-Loop Change Process . . 125
Work Flow, Terminologies and Ownership 126

Change Implementation Plans and Execution 127
Criteria for Assessing and Certifying Software Tools 128
The Meaning of CMII-Compliant Certification . . . 129
Chapter 12 — Summary 130

13 CMII Implementation and ROI　　　　**131**
Preparation Phase and Cross-Functional Teams . . . 132
Define Destination by Tailoring the CMII Model . . 133
Team Member Selection and Training 134
Assessment of Existing Processes and Tools 135
Development of a Transition Plan 136
Implementation Steps and Levels of Proficiency . . . 137
Cost Avoidance Versus Cost Reduction 138
Projected Return-On-Investment 139
First Priority: Eliminate Corrective Action 140
Maquiladora Industry and Offshore Manufacturing . 141
Chapter 13 — Summary 142

14 How to Get Started　　　　**143**
Start With This Book 144
Required Resources Already Exist 145
Core Business Process Owners and Training 146
Easier to Be Forgiven Than to Obtain Permission . . 147
Note: Executive Position to Be Filled 148
Progress, Cost and Benefit Measurements 149
Consideration for Enabling Tools 150
CMII Skills and Supply Versus Demand 151
Chapter 14 — Summary 152

Source for CMII Training 153
Lists of Figures and Tables 154
Glossary of Acronyms and Terms 156
Index 161

1

A Little History and Lessons Learned

Continuous corrective action is not continuous improvement.

Corrective action is a by-product of deficient requirements.

Deficient requirements are a by-product of deficient processes.

Ability to plan and achieve plans is a function of process reliability.

Lead time is a function of capacity and priority.

The principles of capacity planning and priority control must be applied to all processes used throughout the organization.

The company that I joined in the early 1970s had a good product and a solid market. They knew the defense business. In attempting to gain the efficiencies of a commercial enterprise, they were focused on business process improvement — and tools for automating such processes were looking increasingly attractive. We were part of an earlier wave of companies that raced ahead to implement a material requirements planning (MRP) system.

The first few years were filled with frustration but we were not alone. As someone observed at the time, "The ditches along the MRP implementation trail are filled with wrecks." Those fired from one company were hired at the next. A small nucleus of motivated individuals within our company survived and kept it going. Things fell into place. By the late '70s, we had a best practice showcase.

The Environment We Were Trying to Automate

Our company produced costly and complex products, averaging over a half-million dollars each, at a rate of about 60 per month. No two orders were ever alike unless a customer ordered multiple units of the same configuration. Some of the complexity was due to the extreme environments in which the equipment had to operate. We shipped to customers around the world from our build-to-order factory in the United States.

Because many clients would pay anything as long as they got what they wanted quickly, competition was based on product capability, reliability and delivery schedule rather than pricing. The company that could deliver the build-to-order product in the shortest period of time had a tremendous advantage.

Each customer could choose from a long list of options. Sales personnel worked with various customers around the world to prepare a check list of desired options. Other specialists would then translate those saleable features and functions into buildable units. The gaps in the order definition process necessitated countless phone calls between sales and the personnel who had to build, test and ship the products.

Most customers needed installation drawings first so they could prepare the site which might range from a high-rise office building to a pipeline pumping station. Customers typically insisted on receiving these drawings at least two to four months before receipt of the product. Each set of installation drawings was built to order just like the associated products.

Had we waited until receiving orders before purchasing required materials from suppliers, customer lead time would have been more than two years. That was not the case. Standardized modules and options were procured to a forecast and then assembled after receipt of the customer's order.

Product delivery lead time was generally quoted at six months or less while installation drawings were promised to whatever timeline the customer demanded. Our competitors operated on similar schedules. Customers learned that they could not trust our delivery commitments and imposed penalties for late deliveries.

Upstream Processes and Downstream Problems

There are many environments where standard modules and options are built to a forecast and then assembled to customer order. The final assembly line in an automobile company is one example: modules and components are received at one end and the finished products come out the other. Each automobile produced may represent a unique configuration.

Organizations that are in the business of assembling to customer order use a two-level master production schedule. In our company, we dubbed the higher-level schedule a production plan. The subordinate-level schedule was called a master schedule. The production plan was derived from a forecast of the models that could be built and sold in each period. Created to support the production plan, the master schedule defined the quantities of standardized modules and options required in each time period. The options to be included in the master schedule represented another forecast.

A two-level master production schedule is, therefore, a two-level forecast. Our sales department tried to keep the near term periods filled with confirmed orders. And although we used a 2-year production plan, anything beyond one year into the future was purely a forecast. Both the production plan and the master schedule were continually adjusted as actual orders differed from the forecasts.

Engineering changes were also a fact of life. Product designs as well as the processes for producing the products were in a constant state of change. Product options, and the interfaces between them, were continually added, deleted and upgraded. The translations from saleable features and functions to buildable units had to be upgraded accordingly. The change process was not a single integrated process. It was comprised of many processes with many gaps.

It was clear to those responsible for the downstream activities that the upstream processes were out of control. The intervention resources required to rescue quality and schedule were huge. The first step was to understand what the upstream processes were trying to do and where they were deficient. There were obvious deficiencies in both the customer order definition process and the engineering change process.

Concurrent Engineering and Cross-Functional Teams

Any product should be designed in a way that it can be efficiently scheduled, sold, produced and maintained. Although the term concurrent engineering was not formally recognized until 1989, that was one of the first things we had to do in order to fix the upstream processes. It was obvious to us that the development teams needed to be cross-functional. Further, it was essential that those teams be kept in place as new products continued to evolve and their applications continued to expand.

The processes and methods for doing all of this can be highly robust or, as ours were at the time, deeply mired in corrective action. The only salvation was that our competitors were equally enmeshed. For every product shipped to a new site, we usually "shipped" at least two field service engineers along with it. In fact, we spent a lot of intervention resources in the factory to keep the number down to two. We rarely got anything right; we simply got it good enough to ship.

The idea that defects can be eliminated did not gain popularity until the late 1970s. Philip Crosby was not the first to promote that idea but the word spread fast once he published his book, *Quality Is Free*. This represented a major paradigm shift that our organization was not ready for. It was beyond our comprehension as was the just-in-time concept — we were too mired in the just-in-case approach.

Those who worked in our day-to-day operations had difficulty imagining a defect-free environment. We were convinced there would always be a need for expeditors. We would forever be running out to the shipping dock and opening up the crated product to implement one more change. If we missed the truck, we could just instruct the field engineers make the change at the customer's site.

Regardless of all this intervention, we proceeded to focus on how products moved through each phase of their life cycle and the associated processes. In focusing intently on correlating downstream problems with upstream processes, we began to dig beneath the symptoms and identify the root causes. To ensure that our cross-functional team members shared a common perspective, each member was required to go to at least one customer site and participate in the installation and start-up of our equipment.

Build-To-Order With Concurrent Customization

Very few customers were able to select options from our standardized check list and get exactly what they wanted in their product. Most requested additional features and/or functionality. It seemed we continually added extra pages to the customer order form to describe those desired features and functions. Many customer orders were won simply because we were able to accommodate such special requests without seriously compromising the integrity of the product or the delivery schedule.

This is where we learned a very important lesson. One side of the organization was adamant that our products were so highly customized that an attempt to establish standardized modules would be a waste of time. The other side insisted that standardized modules and options, if properly structured, would provide a foundation upon which customization could be accomplished in a much more reliable and efficient manner. The first approach would have taken us down the wrong path; fortunately we chose the latter.

Some customized features must be incorporated at the earliest phase of assembly while others need to be inserted at the appropriate points in the assembly process, and some can wait until the last minute. The objective is to add the customized features at a point sufficiently early to avoid the need for disassembly and reassembly. Properly structured and standardized modules enable the entire series of tasks, including customization, to be more reliable and efficient.

Nothing impeded our ability to reduce customer order lead time more than this customization effort. The first step toward resolution was to establish a separate customer order engineering group which was split off from the product development and sustaining engineering activities. This group was placed in the midst of the production planning activities and focused solely on customization.

This customer order engineering group was comprised of a mix of product design experts and production process experts. We organized a separate team for each model and each truly worked as a team. Their contribution toward improving product reliability and reducing customer order lead time was enormous. They were an important part of the total solution.

Reduced Lead Times Through Capacity Planning

The idea of using capacity planning to reduce supplier reorder lead time, and also improve the supplier's on-time delivery performance, existed in the 1970s. However, the transformation of that idea into a highly efficient process, now known as supply chain management, came later. A brilliant idea at the time it was conceived, capacity planning is prerequisite for achieving just-in-time and zero inventory. The transition from just-in-case to just-in-time in the area of inventory control was led by Japanese firms in the '70s and then copied elsewhere.

Capacity planning is used to ensure that a master production schedule is valid by providing a way to keep work loads balanced with capacity as jobs flow throughout a network of work centers. Capacity planning techniques were developed in a manufacturing job shop environment; the engineering change process is also a job shop environment. The principles of capacity planning and just-in-time are needed in any work center network.

Capacity planning serves to build trust between buyers and suppliers as well. Simply reserve capacity with your suppliers and have them deliver what you need when you need it. Buy specific quantities of each configuration in the near term when you know exactly what you need. Buy capacity in the longer term where forecasts are fuzzy. Use time fences to mark the boundaries.

The just-in-time principles are valid for any business application, not just inventory. Why create a document early and have it sit for an extended period before it is to be used or release an approved change to the implementation activities if its critical path goes through a work center already backlogged with higher-priority jobs? Every activity within an organization has its critical paths. Work centers within the critical paths deserve the most attention.

The transition from just-in-case to just-in-time was a major paradigm shift for buyers and suppliers. That shift has been achieved in the inventory control side of the organization and is now standard practice. An important part of our solution was to make that same shift in all other activities including the engineering change process. This golden nugget of wisdom had to be invented; it did not exist.

Build-To-Print Versus Process Plans

Development activities typically build prototypes from engineering drawings. Suppliers that build components for a prototype may also use engineering drawings as their guide. Once the developed product transitions out of the development phase and into the production phase, such drawings are not likely to be adequate.

Organizations that produce highly complex products often complement their engineering drawings with process plans, which are produced by process engineers. Employees who actually build the product may work exclusively from the process plans. They may never see design documents such as engineering drawings.

A drawing represents how an item should look in its finished state. Certain types of drawings include cross-sectional views as needed to fully describe the item. Parts lists or bills of material identify the materials required to make the item. A process plan is a step-by-step instruction on how to use the production process and specified materials to produce an item that will conform to its design.

Every organization must decide on a program-by-program basis whether or not process plans are needed and if the benefits outweigh the costs. Organizations that have only limited experience with process plans tend to avoid them while those with extensive experience tend to insist on having them. Whether they are worthwhile or not depends upon whom you ask.

At the time of my arrival at the company in the early 1970s, there was a significant staff of process engineers on each of the major business programs. Very few standards existed on how to prepare process plans. There was no standardized process for releasing process plans or changing those that were already released. The process plans were not being validated by anyone other than the process engineers who wrote them. The only signature was that of the process engineer.

By the end of the '70s, all process plans conformed to one common set of standards. Each physical item to be produced had its own process plan. No process plan could be released until it had been validated by both its author and one of its users. Any process plan that was not free of difficulty for each user was flagged for improvement.

Documents and Number of Signatures

One of the most important lessons that we learned during our process improvement efforts revolved around documents and signatures. We found it necessary to determine what a signature is for before we could agree on how many should be required. Some were shocked by our conclusions — specifically those doing all the signing. On the other hand, the users who had not been provided an opportunity to sign were elated by our findings.

One early observation was the questionable integrity of the various documents used in day-to-day activities. No document, regardless of its type, was immune to defects. Many defects were relatively minor but some were not. Our unexpected discovery was that a larger number of signatures did not help to make documents more accurate; they simply slowed down the change process.

We could not resolve the signature issue until we resolved several other issues. Document defects were caused by a variety of factors. One of the first required steps was to assure that superseded documents were always removed from all points of use. (This rule was later included in the ISO 9000 International Quality Standards). A second prerequisite was to make sure work was performed to the correct revision level (another ISO 9000 rule).

Once these basic issues were resolved, we began to zero in on signatures. The number of signatures on a single document ranged from one to many and there was a lot of variation in how they were used. Some people asked to be on the signature list for a specific document as a way to make sure they got a copy when it changed. Some documents had many signatures, none of which were users.

In other cases, an individual could sign the change form used to route a stack of design documents for signatures and thereby approve the entire stack. Change forms used to route the larger stacks often accumulated up to thirty signatures. Again, actual users were often excluded from those signature lists.

Lesson learned: Each document must be properly owned. There can be no single owner; every document must be co-owned and signed by its creator (or author) and one or more users. Relatively simple documents can be co-signed by a creator and a designated user.

Best Practice Built on Refined CM Principles

As we worked our way through the many complex and interdependent processes, we proceeded to identify the gaps and fix them as we believed to be appropriate at that time. Whenever we adjusted or replaced a process, we usually knew we would have to come back and adjust it again. We continually discovered processes and/or dependencies that we did not know about.

The months spent adding, deleting, realigning and adjusting processes turned into years. Our understanding of those processes went through a steady evolution as we continued to take them apart, refine the pieces and put them back together. Changes that did not improve process reliability and efficiency were backed out. Our cross-functional team stayed intact throughout that period which was a major key to our success.

We did not know what the end result would be, or should be, when we started. There were no preconceived ideas of what was possible or how far we would get. We simply knew that a lot of downstream problems needed to be solved. Learning that most of the root causes resided upstream was relatively easy, but also initiated a major step forward. The customer order entry and engineering change processes were most obviously broken. As a result, the downstream processes, whether broken or not, did not have a chance to be reliable and efficient.

It was long after the team members broke up and went their separate ways that we were able to look back and identify what was most important about our effort and what made it successful. As new business process improvement initiatives continued to come along, we were always interested to see if their sponsors had discovered our secrets. These reviews helped us determine what was most important about our accomplishments.

We established the ability to accommodate change and keep all requirements clear, concise and valid. Although an appropriate business process infrastructure is a prerequisite, there was no existing standard. We created our own by building upon the principles of configuration management. Those hard-won nuggets of wisdom led to what is now known as CMII.

Chapter 1 — Summary

The business process infrastructure, as represented by the CMII model, got its roots from a business process improvement effort initiated in the early 1970s. By the end of that decade, we had achieved a business process that was truly a showcase. To an outsider, it might seem that we should be able to provide a road map they could follow and achieve the same results.

We did not have such a map or a clear definition of our destination when we started. We still did not have one when we achieved the showcase process that elated everyone, from our customers and suppliers to our management and follow employees. It took several years before we were able to define the desirable place in which we found ourselves and tell someone else how to get there.

The only thing we knew was the general direction in which we had to go. As we marched along, we were constantly looking for good ideas. We went to professional society meetings and quizzed those who had "been there and done that." We reviewed each of the business process improvement initiatives that came along. Various consultants cycled through from time to time. If there was an idea that we liked, we tried it out; if it did not work, we moved on.

Things began falling into place and our direction became increasingly clear. As our progress continued, we discovered there were fewer and fewer experts who could help us. We were treading where others had never been. If we were going to keep advancing, it was obvious we had to do it on our own. We had to become the experts.

Our journey led us to recognize that the "requirements" were out of control — largely the result of deficiencies in the customer order definition and engineering change processes. Understanding the culture changes and paradigm shifts required to make the needed improvements represented equally important lessons.

Ultimately, however, the most important lesson learned was the criteria for sifting out the best ideas for process improvement. Any idea that improves the ability to "change faster and/or document better" has merit. The best ideas deserve top priority. As of 1988, this approach was given a name: "CMII."

2
CM Paradigms and CMII Principles

Paradigm: An example serving as a model, pattern, mold, standard, ideal, paragon, touchstone. Webster's New World Dictionary

CM: Life cycles begin and end with physical items.
CMII: Life cycles begin and end with documentation.

CM: The primary product of development is a prototype.
CMII: The primary product of development is documentation.

CM: A prototype serves to prove that the design works.
CMII: A prototype serves to proof the documentation.

Although configuration management is where we found key elements required to make the needed business process improvements, those elements were of little value in their existing state. No other business process has as many paradigms that need to be shifted. That is why organizational leaders who happened to look in that area for nuggets of wisdom rarely saw any.

Another major reason is that the first comprehensive book, *The Fundamentals of Configuration Management* by T. T. Samaras and F. L. Czerwinski, was not written until 1971 and its distribution was limited. Both authors had extensive experience with military standards. Most of the books that followed throughout the 1970s and '80s were also a replay of military standards. The emphasis of books written in the past ten years has shifted to software configuration management but the original paradigms still prevail.

Configuration Management as Traditionally Defined

Configuration management was introduced by the U.S. Department of Defense (DoD) in the 1960s and imposed on defense contractors as a way to track what was built and delivered. Suppliers routinely made last minute changes to products and yet failed to update the documentation. Documentation did not match the products delivered. Suppliers could not verify what they had shipped. As a result, the ability to operate and maintain the equipment was at risk.

The solution, configuration management, was first defined by the U.S. Air Force in 1962. That original definition evolved into the definition in Table 2-1, which achieved widespread acceptance.

Configuration Management - *A discipline applying technical and administrative direction and surveillance over the life cycle of configuration items to:*

(1) Identify and document the functional and physical characteristics of configuration items (CI's). *(**Identification**)*

(2) Control changes to CI's and their related documentation. *(**Configuration Control**)*

(3) Record and report information needed to manage CI's effectively, including the status of proposed and approved changes. *(**Status Accounting**)*

(4) Audit CI's to verify conformance to documented requirements. *(**Reviews and Audits**)*   MIL-STD-973, Configuration Management, 17 April, 1992

Table 2-1   Traditional definition of configuration management.

The military standards that provided this definition are no longer active. U.S. Secretary of Defense William Perry issued a directive in June 1994 to replace the military standards with "best commercial practices." The DoD-sponsored replacement standard, EIA/ANSI-649, *National Consensus Standard for CM*, was released in 1998.

This new standard, like its predecessor, is limited to design definition. It is a guidance document with no how-to's. The ability to accommodate change is not emphasized.

CM: A Process for Communicating Formally

An organization that relies on verbal communications to bridge the gaps in its formal flows of information cannot grow and continue to be efficient. The various activities within an organization must learn how to communicate formally; that is, through documents, data, forms and records as shown in Figure 2-1.

Such formalized communications can be very fluent and any gaps can be eliminated. All activities must work with common repositories of information which, in turn, must be subjected to CM. The CM process must be expanded beyond design definition to encompass all information used to run the business.

Configuration management is the process most directly involved in the management of documents, data, forms, records and associated changes. CM is therefore the proper language for communicating formally. Each employee must become proficient in the language of CM wherein terms such as "effectivities" and "interchangeability" are clearly understood.

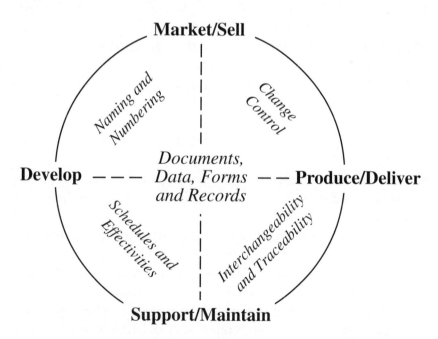

Figure 2-1   Communicate formally via documents, data, forms and records.

Standardized Acronyms and Terminologies

Communication problems arise when an inappropriate word is used or when a word has more than one interpretation. That is why we have dictionaries. It could be assumed that a word does not exist, or should not be used, if it is not in the dictionary. However, we all know of such words used in day-to-day business practices. They simply do not have the widespread use needed to qualify for inclusion. Many terms commonly used by configuration management professionals fall into that category.

Any organization wanting to reach the highest levels of proficiency must standardize upon the terminologies used in its day-to-day activities. This is best accomplished in three steps. First, select a dictionary that can be adopted as the standard for the entire organization. Second, create a glossary of commonly used acronyms, words and phrases which are not included in that dictionary or which have a different definition.

The final step is to establish an operating standard that describes how the dictionary and glossary are to be used and how they are to be kept up-to-date. It is then appropriate to establish a rule whereby any phrase, word or acronym to be used in the organization's documents, data, forms and/or records must first reside in the dictionary or glossary. It is a cost-effective process. The return on investment will be proportional to the degree that the organization is mired in corrective action.

The need for corrective action and the associated intervention resources are eliminated by removing their causes. As any quality professional knows, defects do not just happen, they are caused. If a process is generating defects, the organization must find time to fix the process while correcting the defects.

The appropriate business process infrastructure ensures the reliability and efficiency of all processes used to run the business. It provides a way for activities to communicate formally; thus eliminating gaps and reducing the need for verbal intervention. It also helps ensure that communications are clear and concise. The appropriate dictionary and glossary of terms represent key building blocks within that infrastructure.

Contradicting Definitions of Quality

Requirements and *quality* are key words used repeatedly throughout most organizations. Both can be found in any dictionary and both have a wide range of interpretations. The following definitions of quality arc typical:

> *Quality: (1) any of the features that make something what it is. (2) basic nature, character, kind. (3) degree of excellence which a thing possesses; superiority.*

As of the late 1980s, a fierce debate evolved among quality professionals regarding the proper definition of quality and continues to rage today. The following definitions represent the two opposing sides.

> *Side 1: Quality is conformance to requirements.*
> P. B. Crosby, "Quality is Free," 1979

> *Side 2: Quality is whatever the customer likes.*
> Consensus of several articles and letters to the editor; Quality Progress, 1989

Many quality professionals endorse the second definition because they believe the first undermines what quality is all about. On the other hand, configuration management professionals overwhelmingly endorse Crosby's definition. They would say "get the requirements right and the customer will like the product. Conversely, to not like a product is to not like its requirements."

To configuration management professionals, the first definition achieves the second. It boils down to assuring that requirements are clear, concise and valid. Clear means easy to understand. Concise means all parties have the same interpretation. Valid means the results will be right if the requirements are accomplished to the letter.

Those who support Side 1 believe it is premature to build something if the customer has not validated the requirements. Those holding the opposite view believe meeting requirements does not assure customer satisfaction. Requirements are either important, or not so important, depending on which side you are on.

Requirements Must Lead, Products Must Conform

As of 1986, the U.S. Air Force changed the rules for quality with its suppliers. Its quality control representatives had evolved into a practice of accepting products on the basis of "suitable for use." Any nonconformances to the contractual requirements were otherwise overlooked. The Air Force took a stand, as the quality of the products being accepted was causing problems in the field. Suitable for use was replaced with "must conform to the requirements."

The immediate impact on suppliers was enormous. The Air Force quality control representatives at some supplier sites were suddenly rejecting up to 40 percent of the products that they had normally accepted. The suppliers that were already stretched to the limit suddenly had a lot more work to do. Many of them were already mired in the corrective action mode.

This change in rules came as a shock to many suppliers and forced them to go back to the basics. The problem was not with the contracts. Rather, the suppliers' own internal processes for defining requirements and assuring that products conformed to those requirements needed overhauling. The suppliers were forced to do what they had committed to do; that is, provide products that conformed to their own designs and which the Air Force had validated.

Most mature organizations implement rules to prevent such quality problems from occurring. For example, a document that has not been released cannot be used. If a discrepancy is detected in a released document, work is stopped until the discrepancy is formally corrected. Markups are not acceptable.

It is very difficult for companies to adopt and enforce such rules when they are accustomed to working in a corrective action mode. They fear that such rules would "shut them down." Work would be stopped all the time. They lack confidence in their ability to create good requirements.

Most organizations would like to play by the right rules but are afraid of them so they allow the product to lead. If the documentation does not catch up, they write a deviation. As a result, they dig themselves deeper into the corrective action mode. To reverse the trend, they must learn how to create and maintain good requirements.

Stove-Pipe Processes and Stand-Alone Systems

The amount of money spent on business process automation has increased annually since such tools became available decades ago. Many organizations, however, continue to be dissatisfied with the overall functionality of both the tools and their user friendliness. The system implemented last year is this year's legacy system. The system implemented this year will earn that reputation next year. Integrated systems with seamless interfaces are still an elusive goal.

The frustration and huge amount of waste will continue until priorities are realigned. Current strategies for automation, per Figure 2-2, are bypassing the processes for managing requirements because those processes are generally fragmented and informal in nature.

Such fragmentation is fixed by establishing the appropriate business process infrastructure and using that infrastructure to drive the strategy for automation. Inability to keep requirements in the lead is a symptom that the existing infrastructure is inadequate. This must be solved before the automation goals can be achieved.

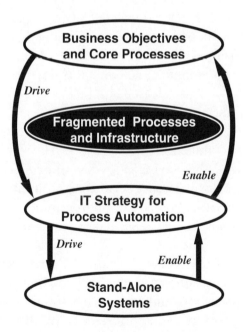

Figure 2-2   Stand-alone systems: byproduct of stove-pipe processes.

Fixed Baselines Versus Moving Baselines

Traditional approaches to configuration management used fixed baselines to manage product design definition as it evolved during the development process. Each development effort went through a series of four, five or six milestones. Overall development progress was monitored in terms of milestones, associated baselines and approved changes to the baseline.

The evolving design definition was brought up-to-date at each milestone by incorporating all changes that had been approved since the previous baseline. Once all parties agreed on the baseline, the development effort could proceed into the next phase. The current design, at any point in time, was therefore represented by the most recently approved baseline plus approved changes.

Once the development effort proceeds past a fixed baseline and into the next phase, the design definition becomes increasingly fuzzy. It becomes fuzzy because a baseline is a collection of many documents and any number of those documents may have unincorporated changes. To determine the status of any one document, it is necessary to retrieve that document and any changes, and determine what it would be with those changes incorporated.

Fixed baselines represent what the evolving product design was at a specific point in time, not what it is now or what it is going to be. As-planned and as-released baselines represent a much better approach. They are moving baselines in that they are updated with each approved change. The as-released portion contains released documents with no unincorporated changes. The as-planned portion contains documents that are in the process of being released.

Another major difference between fixed and moving baselines is that fixed baselines are limited to design definition. As-planned and as-released baselines include all design and process-related information for each physical item residing at each level in the hierarchy.

As-planned and as-released baselines are a cornerstone of the ideal business process infrastructure. Such moving baselines make it relatively easy to see the overall status of a baseline as it evolves. They also simplify the effort required to assess the overall impact of a change.

One Standardized, Enterprise-Wide Change Process

Very few organizations use one common change process to update the full spectrum of documents used in their day-to-day activities. Although most organizations have an "engineering change process," its scope is typically limited to design definition. Other activities have their own specific processes for creating and maintaining various types of documents.

For example, process plans which provide step-by-step instructions for producing a product are typically created and maintained by process engineering. Manuals for how to operate and maintain fielded equipment are typically created and maintained by a product support function. Procedures for how to perform administrative tasks are typically created and maintained by another function. Most organizations have multiple change processes accordingly.

Such fragmentation is a primary reason most engineering change process improvement efforts die in futility. There is little benefit in improving one process if its integration with the other processes is not also improved. However, it is impossible to improve the overall change process until the various types of information used to run the business are properly integrated, structured and made visible to all parties. This prerequisite is achieved with the as-planned and as-released baselines.

Physical item hierarchies provide the framework for product-oriented baselines. Each item residing at each level in the hierarchy is linked to its full range of supporting documentation. Such baselines make it possible to see the total impact of a change. They make it possible to create an implementation road map identifying the specific documents that must be upgraded. They also provide a way to keep the various information sets properly synchronized.

Establishing the appropriate baselines does not fix the change process, it only makes the desired change process possible. All changes go through an analysis phase and, if approved, an implementation phase. Both phases become relatively easy when it is possible to see the impact of a change across the full spectrum of physical items and associated documents. The appropriate baselines make it possible to achieve one common, enterprise-wide change process.

Potential Conflicts With Cost Accounting

The basic task of cost accounting within a business enterprise is to identify and report costs relative to revenues. In the case of a manufacturing environment, revenues and costs are compiled for each like-family of products that are built, sold and delivered on a period-by-period basis. Overall costs are typically segregated into material, direct labor and overhead increments.

The potential conflicts between configuration management and cost accounting arise in how identification numbers are used to identify and track physical items as they move through the manufacturing process. Configuration management uses those identification numbers to identify and link physical items to their supporting documentation and to also control interchangeability.

Cost accounting uses those same identification numbers to track and report costs. Its preferences for assigning and changing item identification numbers are not always compatible with the preferences of configuration management.

For example, less than ten years ago government agencies required defense contractors to segregate costs by contract. Physical items used in government contracts could not be placed in the same inventory location with identical items used in commercial applications. Not only did this rule inflate inventory and handling costs, it also compromised the producer's ability to take advantage of the price breaks normally achieved with volume purchases. Although such items were interchangeable from a CM point of view, they were not interchangeable from a cost accounting point of view.

The underlying issue stems from how physical item identification numbers are used. Configuration management and cost accounting are only two of the many activities that must work together and establish rules that best serve the needs of all parties. Proper naming and numbering conventions are a very important part of the total solution but no widely accepted book has ever been written on either subject.

CM Reinvented

Traditional approaches to configuration management are oriented toward controlling change whereas CMII is oriented toward accommodating change. Although changes in both cases are managed relative to requirements, these two paths are very different.

Under the traditional approaches, requirements and associated changes were limited to design definition. The scope of CMII includes all design and process-related information that could impact safety, quality, schedule, cost, profit or the environment. The definition of CMII is derived accordingly, per Table 2-2.

Configuration management (CM) is the process of managing an organization's products, facilities and processes by managing their requirements, including changes, and assuring that results conform in each case. CMII expands the scope of CM to encompass all information that could impact safety, quality, schedule, cost, profit or the environment. CMII shifts the emphasis of CM to (1) accommodating change, (2) accommodating the reuse of standards and best practices, (3) assuring that all requirements remain clear, concise and valid, (4) communicating (1), (2) and (3) to each user promptly and precisely and (5) assuring conformance in each case. Process improvement, per CMII, is measured by ability to "change faster and/or document better." *As evolved from 1988 - 2002*

Table 2-2   Definition of CM and CMII.

To transition from the traditional approach of configuration management to the CMII approach requires the shift of many paradigms. Resistance to this shift was already eroding before cancellation of the military standards was initiated in 1994. Most of the "old-pros" saw the value and endorsed the principles very quickly.

Acceptance of CMII has continued to accelerate. It is now acknowledged by many well-known business enterprises and government agencies to epitomize the best configuration management practice and business process infrastructure.

Chapter 2 — Summary

Configuration management is where we found the key elements required to make the needed business process improvements, but those elements had only limited value in their existing state. No other business process had as many paradigms that needed to be shifted. That is one reason that those striving to improve their business processes, and who happened to look in that area for nuggets of wisdom, rarely saw any.

It became necessary to reinvent configuration management. Traditional approaches to configuration management had to be shifted from controlling change to accommodating change. Although changes in both cases are managed relative to requirements, these two paths are very different.

Under the traditional approaches, requirements and associated changes were limited to design definition. To be most successful, an organization must manage all information which could impact safety, quality, schedule, cost, profit or the environment. This means that all process-related information must also be managed effectively. CMII expands the scope of CM accordingly.

Change is universal and the only constant. The organization that is best at accommodating change and keeping requirements clear, concise and valid will eventually win. The various activities within an organization must learn how to communicate formally through documents, data, forms and records. Configuration management is the proper language for doing that.

To put the proper configuration management process in place is to build the appropriate business process infrastructure. To build such an infrastructure includes replacing fixed baselines with moving baselines that contain all design and process-related information. It includes standardizing on an enterprise-wide change process for maintaining those baselines and the associated information.

The business process infrastructure, once properly established, must be used to drive the strategy for automating the business processes. The ability to achieve totally integrated systems with seamless interfaces will continue to be an elusive goal until the proper infrastructure has been established.

3

Proof that CM Is, or Is Not, Working

Working harder just to stay even.

Too busy fighting alligators to drain the swamp.

There is not enough time to do it right the first time but there is always time to redo it until it is "suitable for use."

When CM is working, everything works.
When CM is not working, nothing works.

A clear definition of the problem is 90% of the solution.

Many organizations are gaining an appreciation of the importance of configuration management and the role that it should play. Most organizations have a few individuals who understand the role that CM needs to play but they are typically in the minority. The importance of good CM needs to be made clear to all parties.

This chapter contains examples of well-publicized failures to apply CM principles followed by a few brief success stories. The degree of success or failure is revealed in terms of safety, quality, schedule, cost and/or profit. The objective is to identify the causes for failure and why those causes did not also derail the successes.

These examples of successes and failures were selected at random. It is very likely that the same conclusions would have been derived from any other set of examples because there is a common CM thread that runs through all successes and failures.

Sorting Symptoms From Root Causes

Problems do not simply happen, they are caused. Problems are by-products of invalid processes and/or broken rules. Once the processes and rules used to run the business are thoroughly understood, it is possible to identify the types of problems, if any, that should be expected. Any problems that do occur should rarely be a surprise.

The appropriate processes and rules are those which minimize the chance for problems to happen. They also facilitate quick identification of the root causes if and when a problem does occur. Table 3-1 provides a list of operational guidelines and/or rules which serve this dual purpose.

- *The organization is requirements-driven.*
- *Data integrity is measured and assured.*
- *Intervention resources are measured relative to goals.*
- *Physical items must conform to released requirements.*
- *Each physical item is linked to its design and process documents.*
- *Each document is a requirement to its user.*
- *Documents are released before they are used.*
- *Documents are validated before they are released.*
- *Each document is co-owned by its creator and a user.*
- *Numbering conventions are used to control interchangeability.*
- *Naming conventions are used to identify similarities for reuse.*
- *The change process is closed-loop and self-correcting.*
- *The change process includes a fast-track capability.*
- *Business decisions are separate from implementation details.*
- *Appropriate records are a by-product of each process.*

Table 3-1   CMII operating guidelines and/or rules.

Financial statements and balance sheets do not reveal the degree to which an organization is suffocating on corrective action. Insiders who work in the downstream trenches and deal with corrective action each day have the best insight into the magnitude of the problems. Most problems can be traced back to deficiencies in one or more of these operating guidelines and/or rules.

Software Development: Statistics for 1995

Problems with development programs have increased in magnitude as software content has increased. A survey by the Standish Group, per Table 3-2, provides insight to software development performance during 1995. (They note that prior years were worse).

In 1995, the U.S. government and businesses spent approximately $81 billion on cancelled software projects and another $59 billion for budget overruns. About one-sixth of all projects were completed on time and within budget, nearly one-third were cancelled outright and over half were considered "challenged." Of the challenged or cancelled projects, the average project was 189% over budget and 222% behind schedule. Failures are attributed, in no particular order, to

- *poor user input,*
- *stakeholder conflicts,*
- *vague requirements,*
- *poor cost and schedule estimates,*
- *inadequate skills,*
- *cutting jobs and expecting the same work,*
- *failure to plan,*
- *communication breakdowns,*
- *poor architecture and*
- *late failure warning signals.*

The Standish Group, "Chaos," 1995, http://www.standishgroup.com/chaos.html

---

Table 3-2   Statistics on software development in the U.S. for 1995.

The authors did a good job of quantifying the problem and listing possible contributing causes. The causes need to be explored in more depth. Some are more significant than others.

Many of the listed causes are highly interdependent and several are directly related to configuration management. A search for root causes should begin with determining why the requirements were vague. Such an exercise would reveal a wealth of valuable information.

Motor Vehicle Computer System Fiasco

The development problems described in Table 3-3 represented a relatively simple computer program. The technical challenge did not "push the state of the art" yet it became a major embarrassment to all parties involved.

Getting your car's title and registration was supposed to go high tech today. But the Arizona Motor Vehicle Division can't make a Sept. 25 deadline to start the first phase of its new $30 million computer system. The system is more than a year behind schedule, and the cost has ballooned to triple the original estimate.

"We don't want to turn this on until we feel comfortable it will perform," project leader Timothy Wolfe said. The latest hang-up is getting the software to sort through all the data that the division has on file. MVD's database is mammoth; it consists of the records on 6 million vehicles. All that information has been converted from one computer language to another, but it still needs "tuning up."

The information isn't indexed so that the computer can sort through it easily to find a Vehicle Identification Number, or VIN. Tracking down a single VIN has taken 10 to 20 minutes in trial runs. Picture the problem this way: You want to find a particular book at the library. So you check every single shelf in the building instead of finding the location of the book in the card catalog.

The project started five years ago with the goal of integrating the computer systems that handle titles and registration, driver's licenses and revenues from commercial vehicles. But the job bogged down in software difficulties and personnel problems. The commercial-vehicle part of the project was dropped, and the driver's license portion was put off until August 1996.

"High tech on hold at Motor Vehicle," Arizona Republic, September 25, 1995, by Kathleen Ingley, Staff writer

---

Table 3-3   Motor vehicle division computer system development fiasco.

It is apparent that this project was not requirements-driven. It would appear that the Motor Vehicle Division did not get specific about requirements until after realizing it was not getting what they needed. The software developer then proceeded to treat each clarification of the requirements as a change. Schedules slipped and costs escalated accordingly. It can be concluded that there was little, if any, configuration management at work.

FBI's Fiasco With Records

Although the FBI maintains records of its investigations, the processes for maintaining and retrieving those records is apparently less than perfect. Table 3-4 describes the results of a recent case in which the FBI was directed to submit a specific set of records.

The FBI ordered its field offices four times to turn over to prosecutors any material they gathered during the investigation of the Oklahoma City bombing. But it was only in response to a fifth directive, sent in December, that field offices discovered they had overlooked thousands of pages of documents.

They were unable to explain why the earlier searches failed to turn up all of the material. But others familiar with the case said it appeared to be the result of a sloppy data storage and retrieval system that the FBI was warned about in 1999.

"I just see poor management and bad databases and, unfortunately, an element of incompetence," said Michael Bromwich, a former Justice Department inspector general.

The document problem was widespread, affecting 46 of the FBI's 56 field offices across the country. In a letter to McVeigh's lawyers, Justice Department lawyer Sean Connelly listed 3,135 pages of documents and other items of evidence that had not been turned over to the defense before McVeigh's 1997 trial.

Joe Cantamessa, former chief of the FBI's Investigative Automation Section who now works for Raytheon, said that "while the FBI may have a records system that is often termed antiquated, that does not adequately satisfy what I believe are the underlying causes of this error." FBI Flub Tied to Data Bases - - Incompetence, Arizona Republic, May 12, 2001

Table 3-4   Difficulty experienced by the FBI in retrieving records.

The appropriate processes for performing important work are those which also create appropriate records as a by-product. Such records are retained on a just-in-case basis. They must be properly identified and linked if their retrieval is to be reliable and efficient. The FBI's records system appears to be underdeveloped in this regard.

Air Traffic Control System Fiasco

The problems that the Federal Aviation Administration has experienced in trying to improve the air traffic control system have been extensive, as described in Table 3-5. Although this article was written in 1993, the lessons to be learned are still valid today.

In January 1982, the Federal Aviation Administration proposed a $32 billion overhaul of the air traffic control system. But today, the new system is still at least nine years from completion and already $1.5 billion over its original budget and climbing. The FAA and IBM's Federal Systems Division, the prime contractor, now say the system won't be in place until well after 2000.

In March 1989, IBM and the FAA finally got to work. IBM's initial raw material was a four-foot-high stack of specifications. They spent more than a year refining the specs. It became obvious after a few months that controllers should have more say in the design. They bombarded the FAA and IBM with proposed changes.

The real software writing didn't begin until several months later and was slowed by a steady stream of change orders. As IBM finished one block of software, programmers would have to rewrite an earlier block. IBM didn't protest, partly because it would only add to the delays. IBMers were beginning to take shortcuts such as skipping software reviews to keep the project on its already-delayed schedule. In April 1993, the FAA froze the specs.

"Flying In Place: The FAA's Air-Control Fiasco," By Mark Lewyn, Business Week, April 26, 1993

Table 3-5   Air traffic control system requirements and change management.

A major portion of the many air traffic control system problems would appear to be due to deficiencies in the requirements and change management processes. Such poor performance was certainly unexpected since IBM's Federal Systems Division was the premier software developer during the 1980s and many organizations have adopted its practices. Loral took over the air traffic control work when it acquired the Federal Systems Division in 1994.

Random Failures or Is Something Terribly Wrong?

This was the question asked by industry analysts after a succession of failures rocked the space program (Table 3-6).

After experiencing three failed Titan IV missions in a row and other difficulties over the past nine months, Astronautics and its 9,500 employees are having a crisis of confidence. Some observers have questioned whether pressures to drive down costs over the past decade and the resulting job cuts may have deprived the company of talented, experienced employees.

Designing and manufacturing rockets is not the same as assembly-line production, said John Logsdon, director of the space policy institute at George Washington University. "To successfully build them, elements of craft, judgment and experience must come into play," he said.

Earlier this month, Lockheed Martin appointed a panel to review engineering, manufacturing, quality control and program management in the company. Logsdon said "Lockheed is doing the right thing. There does seem to be some systemic problem."

Steven Aftergood, research analyst for the Federation of American Scientists in Washington agreed. He said, "This may be a series of random failures but one can't assume that is the case - the working assumption has to be that something is terribly wrong and in need of fixing."   *"Lockheed Launches Review," The Denver Post, May 16, 1999*

Table 3-6   Difficulties with the Titan IV rocket and its reliability.

The obvious question that needs to be asked is, "How can you know you have a reliable and repetitive process if that process is dependent upon craft, judgment and experience?" The investigation of the various processes used to produce the missiles undoubtedly addressed that issue.

There is no substitute for knowing the reliability of your processes and where the gaps are, if any exist. Once an organization truly understands its processes, there should be no surprises. Clearly, Titan IV's three failed launches represent three enormous surprises.

Safety as Vehicle for Transforming a Company

The success story described in Table 3-7, although highly abbreviated, clearly illustrates the importance of "process" and vigorous employee involvement in process improvement.

Alcoa was in trouble when O'Neill was named CEO in 1987. Like most of America's Rust Belt, Alcoa had quality and productivity problems, aging plants and equipment, a feisty union and profitability concerns.

O'Neill chose safety as his first priority. He wanted the workers on his side. He knew that without them, he could not transform the company. He knew that if Alcoa overhauled its processes in pursuit of safety considerations, the improvements also would affect yield, productivity, quality, inventories, customer responsiveness and other critical performance areas.

Alcoa's safety was running at 2.87 work loss incidents per 100 employees. O'Neill set the goal at zero. Predictable responses included all the reasons that such a goal is not possible, from "you can't make all workers follow procedures," to "the law of diminishing returns." He asked, "How many of our valuable workers should we plan on maiming and killing this year?"

Alcoa's work loss incidents plummeted from 2.87 in 1986 to .013 in 2000, a 95% reduction. But in addition to improving health and safety, there have been radical improvements in yield, productivity, inventories, customer satisfaction, defect-reduction and market share, to name a few. O'Neill started pushing "drive-to-zero" thinking into health care and education as he approached retirement during the late 1990s.

"Perfection is Possible" by Jim Buckman, Star Tribune, May 15, 2000

Table 3-7   Process improvement with zero work-loss incidents as the driver.

This condensed article makes it very clear that the six criteria for measuring success — safety, quality, schedule, cost, profit or the environment, are highly interdependent. Any improvement that helps one will help the other five.

An Organization Serious About Bug-Free Software

Lockheed Martin's Space Mission Systems Division at the Johnson Space Center writes the software for the space shuttle. The division's process-approach has been very successful as the abbreviated article in Table 3-8 details.

How much work the software does is not what makes it remarkable, its how well the software works. It never crashes. It never needs to be rebooted. It is bug-free. It is as perfect as human beings have achieved. Consider these stats: the last three versions of the program, each 420,000 lines long, had just one error each. The last 11 versions had a total of 17 errors. Commercial programs of equivalent complexity would have 5,000 errors.

How do they write the right stuff? It's the process. The group's most important creation is not the perfect software they write, it's the process they invented that writes the perfect software. The process can be reduced to four simple propositions:

1. The product is only as good as the plan for the product. About one-third of the process for writing software happens before anyone writes a line of code. They agree in the most minute detail about everything the new code is supposed to do - - and commit that understanding to paper with the kind of specificity and precision usually found in blueprints. Nothing in the spec's is changed without agreement from both sides. And no coder changes a line of code without spec's carefully outlining the change.

2. The best teamwork is a healthy rivalry between those who write the code and the verifiers who try to find flaws. The shuttle group finds 85% of its errors before formal testing begins.

3. The database is the software base. There is the software and there are the two enormous databases beneath the software. One is the history of the code. The other is a record of every error that has ever been made while writing or working on the software.

4. Don't just fix the mistake, fix whatever permitted the mistake. "They Write the Right Stuff," by Charles Fishman, Fast Company, Dec, 1996

Table 3-8   Development where design leads and software products conform.

32   CMII

Pay a Little Now or Much More Later

Table 3-9 contains excerpts from a book by a recognized authority on the right ways and wrong ways to develop software.

This book is about using effective software development processes. This means:
- *committing all requirements to writing;*
- *a systematic procedure to control additions and changes;*
- *systematic technical reviews of all designs and code;*
- *developing a quality assurance plan early in the project;*
- *creating an implementation plan;*
- *using automated source code control;*
- *updating cost and schedule estimates at each milestone.*

The word "process" is viewed as a four-letter word by some people in the software development community. They see processes as rigid, restrictive and inefficient. They would rather do technical work than spend time planning. But failure to plan is one of the most critical mistakes a project can make.

Success in software development depends on making a carefully planned series of small mistakes in order to avoid making unplanned large mistakes. Exploring four design alternatives and discarding three of them amounts to making three small mistakes. Not doing enough design work and rewriting the code three times amounts to making three large mistakes. Each day a developer spends reviewing project requirements or architecture will typically save 3 to 10 days later in the project.

"Software Project Survival Guide" ©1998, by Steve McConnell

Table 3-9   Software development and the power of process.

Steve McConnell is also the author of *Code Complete* (1993) and *Rapid Development* (1996), both winners of *Software Development* magazine's Jolt award.

Some of our CMII graduates, who have also read Steve's Survival Guide, have asked if he holds CMII certification. Although Steve has not attended our training, he does promote many of the same principles. We highly recommend his books.

Software Process Improvement Statistics

The software development statistics for the United States in the year 1995 would have been worse without the successes that a few organizations were achieving in that same time frame. Some of those successes are summarized in Table 3-10.

Organizations that have explicitly focused on improving their development processes have cut their time-to-market by about one-half and reduced their costs and defects by a factor of 3 to 10. Over a 5-year period, Lockheed cut its development costs by 75%, reduced its time-to-market by 40%, and reduced its defects by 90%. Over a 6.5 year period, Raytheon tripled its productivity and realized a return on investment (ROI) in process improvement of almost 8 to 1. Bull HN realized an ROI of 4 to 1 after 4 years, and Schlumberger realized an ROI of almost 9 to 1 after 3.5 years. NASA's Software Engineering Laboratory cut its average cost per mission by 50% and its defects rate by 75% over an 8-year period while dramatically increasing the complexity of software used on each mission. Similar results have been reported at Hughes, Loral, Motorola, Xerox and other companies.

Companies that have focused on process have found that effective processes support creativity and morale. In a survey of about 50 companies, only 20% in the least process-oriented companies rated their staff morale as "good" or "excellent." In organizations that paid more attention to their software processes, about 50% rated their staff morale as good or excellent. And in the most process-sophisticated organizations, 60% of the people rated their morale as good or excellent.

Pages 26 and 27, "Software Project Survival Guide" ©1998, by Steve McConnell

---

Table 3-10   Examples of benefits derived from software process improvement.

The underlying message throughout these examples of successes and failures should now be coming clear. Good configuration management is a prerequisite to success. When configuration management is working, everything seems to work. When configuration management is not working, nothing seems to work.

Chapter 3 — Summary

This chapter has provided several examples of organizational successes and failures. The degree of success or failure in each case was revealed in terms of safety, quality, schedule, cost or profit. The objective was to look at each example and determine if there were any common threads.

Although the examples were abbreviated, it is nevertheless possible to draw some rather firm conclusions. One very obvious difference between the successes and failures can be attributed to how the requirements were managed. The organizations that had the best success also did the best job of managing their requirements.

Another key difference between the successes and failures was the emphasis that was placed on process. The organizations that have the best success also placed the greatest emphasis on process.

The emphasis on process and ability to manage requirements is summarized very well in the statement "the product is only as good as the plan for the product." From a configuration management point of view, the word *plan* is synonymous with the word *requirements*. Requirements represent plans. Plans represent requirements.

Another statement that proved to be a key building block for success was "They agree in the most minute detail about everything the new code is supposed to do - - and commit that understanding to paper with the kind of specificity and precision usually found in blueprints. Nothing in the spec's is changed without agreement from both sides. And no coder changes a line of code without spec's carefully outlining the change."

The underlying message throughout these examples of successes and failures should now be coming clear. Good configuration management is a prerequisite to success. When configuration management is working, everything seems to work. When configuration management is not working, nothing seems to work.

Problems do not simply happen, they are caused. Problems are by-products of invalid processes and/or broken rules. Once the processes and rules used to run the business are thoroughly understood, it is possible to identify the types of problems that should be expected. Any problems that do occur should rarely be a surprise.

4

CM Subprocesses and Terminologies

CMII is configuration management, project management and quality assurance integrated into one cohesive unit.

The activities of configuration management include:
- *requirements management,*
- *change management,*
- *release management,*
- *data management,*
- *records management,*
- *document control and*
- *library management.*

CMII is more than project management. It is more than quality assurance. It includes the configuration management activities which provide the infrastructure for both project management and quality assurance. It was necessary to reinvent configuration management in order to provide the infrastructure that was needed. CMII evolved from that evolution.

It was necessary to lift configuration management out of its engineering design orientation and give it an enterprise-wide perspective. It was necessary to identify the pockets of configuration management-related activities that exist under various names throughout the organization and bring them together under one umbrella.

The how-to was driven by a common organizational objective to "change faster and document better." This objective provides a sound basis for sifting out the best ideas for process improvement.

Project Management: Two Cycles, not One

Project management is often defined as a closed-loop cycle comprised of four steps as shown in Figure 4-1.

Figure 4-1   Shewhart (or Deming) cycle for project management.

From a CM point of view, project management is two cycles, not one, as shown in Figure 4-2. Requirements planning represents one cycle. The process of performing work on physical items and achieving the as-planned requirements is a separate cycle. These dual cycles are interdependent and must be kept synchronized.

The challenge is to keep the requirements cycle in the lead. A fast and efficient change process, and the ability to keep the upgraded requirements clear, concise and valid, are prerequisites. Traditional approaches to CM lack this capability.

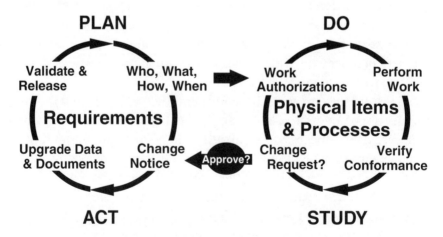

Figure 4-2   Dual-cycle project management per CMII.

Quality: Change Definition or Fix Problem

As discussed on page 15, there is an ongoing debate about the proper definition of quality. Whether quality is defined as "conformance to requirements" or "whatever the customer likes," does not matter from a CMII point of view. Every product must conform to its requirements. To dislike a product is to dislike its requirements. To improve a product is to improve its requirements. Continuous improvement of a product is achieved by continuously improving its requirements.

The first challenge is to build the right product. The right product is represented by the design definition. The second challenge is to build the product right. The right way to build the product is represented by the associated process definition. The degree to which the right product is being built is proportional to the integrity of the design definition. The degree to which the product is built right is proportional to the integrity of the process definition.

It is difficult, if not impossible, to know that the right product is being built when the design definition is vague. It is similarly impossible to verify that a product conforms to its requirements if those requirements are vague or subject to interpretation.

It is also difficult, if not impossible, to build the product right if the associated process definition is vague or subject to interpretation. Even if the process definition is clear and concise, there is still no certainty that the right product is being built if the design is vague.

Those who do not trust the integrity of their product designs and processes are inclined to believe that "quality is whatever the customer likes." They reject that "quality is conformance to requirements" for the same reasons. They do not trust that documented designs and processes can be fixed. The preferred definition is influenced by confidence in the requirements.

Configuration management professionals understand the importance of clear, concise and valid requirements. In order to fix the requirements, it is necessary to fix the configuration management process. The traditional approaches to CM are not the answer. It is necessary to bring all of the CM-related elements together under one umbrella.

Language of CMII: Lowest Common Denominators

To speak the CMII language is to speak in terms of lowest common denominators. They are the same for every organization. In the world of CMII, everything can be subdivided into four categories: *(1) physical items, (2) documents, (3) forms and (4) records*. Each category can be further subdivided by type.

Physical items are identified by an identification number, name and description. Some items may include a model number and/or serial number. Items that carry the same identification number are fully interchangeable. Physical items may be further subdivided by type such as end-item, assembly, subassembly, component, raw material, software program, source code, and so on.

Documents are identified by type, number and revision level. Document types include specifications, schematics, drawings, bills of material, process plans, manuals, etc. Documents of different types may carry the same identification number. A revision level is assigned when a document is initially released and is advanced with each revision. Proper ownership of each document is essential.

Forms include problem reports, enterprise change requests (ECRs), enterprise change notices (ECNs), document change records (DCRs) and work authorizations such as purchase orders, shop orders, test orders, modification orders, and so on. ECNs are used to implement approved ECRs and provide the authority to upgrade released information. Work authorizations provide the authority to perform work on physical items. All work is positively controlled with forms.

Records are comprised of completed forms and referenced documents. Three basic types of records include release records, revision records and as-built records. Each type of record is a by-product of the associated process. Each set of records includes a statement of work, evidence that the work was authorized and that the results did, in fact, conform to the requirements. Any accepted non-onformances are noted and described.

Terms such as *objects* and *classes* cause confusion and are avoided. This becomes an issue during automation efforts because those terms are commonly used by Information Technology.

Requirements Management

Products are designed top-down and built bottom-up as illustrated in Figure 4-3. The left side of the "V-diagram" represents the hierarchy of requirements. The right side represents a corresponding hierarchy of as-built items. The left side represents the as-planned side. The right side is the as-built side. Product and process requirements are validated. Product conformance is verified.

Any defect found on the as-built side is a symptom of deficiencies in the requirements on the left side. Changes initiated on the right side are for corrective action reasons.

Changes initiated on the left side serve to extend higher-level requirements into detailed requirements and/or to improve existing requirements. The goal is to reduce the changes initiated for corrective action reasons to zero.

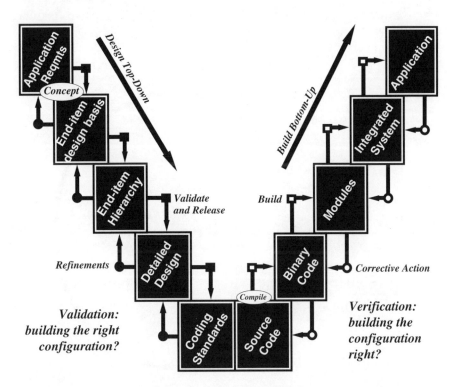

Figure 4-3   V-diagram of development: design top-down, build bottom-up.

Change Management

As-planned and as-released baselines are the cornerstone to the CMII process. The primary purpose of the change process is to create and maintain those baselines and all associated repositories of information. It is appropriate to think of change management as the "backbone" of requirements management. The change management process must be closely coupled with the as-planned and as-released baselines.

The appropriate change process is closed-loop and revolves around the as-planned and as-released baselines. The closed-loop change process also includes a "fast-track" capability. Overall change process efficiency is highly dependent upon how each physical item and each document contained in the baselines is identified, structured, linked and owned.

A closed-loop process is a self-correcting process. Each change that enters the process is tracked through each step to its proper completion. Appropriate release records and change records are a by-product of the process.

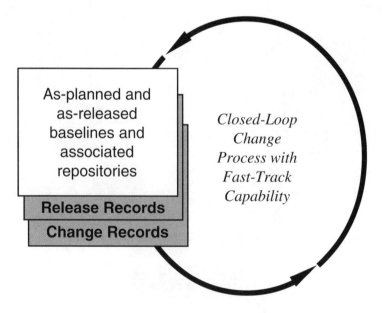

Figure 4-4   Closed-loop change process closely coupled with baselines.

Release Management

*Release: to permit to be issued, shown, published, broadcast,
etc; to put into circulation.*   Webster's New World Dictionary

Release is an important word within the discipline of configuration management. Various activities use the word in various ways.
Its usage needs to be standardized. The preferred use is defined by
showing how it applies to the lowest common denominators, physical
items, documents, forms and records. The needed paradigm shift, if
any, is likely to revolve around its association with physical items.

Documents are released. Each document to be released must
have an enterprise change notice authority. A document must be
released before it can be used. A document must also be validated
before it can be released. A released document cannot be changed
without proper authority.

Forms are released. Forms are used to authorize work. A
form is released when it is issued to initiate work. An enterprise
change request (ECR) form provides the authorization to conduct
technical review and compile cost estimates associated with technical
recommendations. An ECN provides the authorization to implement
approved ECRs. Purchase orders provide authorization to outside
suppliers to supply products and/or services. Shop orders do the same
for internal activities.

Physical items are not released. As-built items are accepted
or rejected. They are accepted once they conform to their released
requirements. A physical item that does not conform may still be
accepted if it is concluded to be suitable for use. Physical items that
are accepted in a production environment are shipped to customers
and accepted by those customers.

Records are not released. Records are accepted or rejected.
Records are accepted once they are accurate and complete. Records
are a by-product of processes which involve released documents and
released forms. Records are not changed once they are accepted.
Records are supplemented with additional records as required. Each
type of record is retained for a specified period of time. Records may
be retrieved and reviewed at any time per the requirements.

Data Management

Data management initially evolved in parallel with configuration management within the U.S. Department of Defense. Configuration management represented how contractors and contracting agencies would manage evolving design definition and associated changes during development and follow-on life cycle phases. Data management represented how such evolving technical data would be transmitted between the contracting agency and contractors. Formal data transmittal standards evolved accordingly.

The data management process has undergone tremendous changes as paper documents transitioned to a digitized state. Evolving product data management tools, document imaging standards and data exchange standards are included in this ongoing transition. Key issues include the movement of data from one type of computer to another and retrieval of information stored on older data bases with newer tools. The Internet brought a new rush of advancements.

The benefits of these improving capabilities have been huge. As equipment becomes increasingly sophisticated, there is an increasing need for access to design, operation and maintenance information. Huge manuals and documents have been replaced by computer terminals. Table 4-1 contains two help wanted ads which help to describe the role that data managers are expected to perform. It is noted that data integrity is emphasized in the ad on the left.

Data Manager	Data Manager
Responsible for the design, development, implementation and management of systems and processes for data management in support of clinical and economic studies. Interface with management staff and investigators re data collection and data transfer. Manage data entry, verification, validation and transfer according to divisional SOPs. Provide clean, reliable and valid data in a timely fashion for analysis, reports, etc. E-mail resume to - - -.	Responsible for developing schedule of contract deliverables and co-ordinating deliveries with contractor data managers. Accept receipt of deliverables, review material to assure compliance with CDRL requirements, load documents into a DM library and notify project office of items that must be reviewed prior to acceptance. Interface with government and contractor personnel and maintain status of deliverables. FAX resume to - - -.

http://jobsearch.monster.com/, August 22, 2001

Table 4-1   Examples of help wanted advertisements for data managers.

Records Management

Records serve to provide evidence that specific work was performed and the desired results were achieved. Various types of records include contracts, legal agreements, release records, change records, as-built records, as-shipped records, modification records, test records, safety records, etc.

Records are used to prove that facilities, equipment and processes within a work environment conform to their requirements and are therefore safe. They are used to prove that products shipped to customers did, in fact, conform to their requirements and are as they were supposed to be. Records are retrieved for review and analysis anytime there is a safety spill, quality spill or other potential liability issue.

If there was never a problem, such records might never be needed. Records are retained on a just-in-case basis. They get little attention when things are going well and a lot of attention when things are not going well. The goal of the records management process is to produce and maintain adequate records and do so at a minimal cost.

Table 4-2 provides examples of help wanted ads which help to describe the type of role that records management personnel are expected to perform. It is obvious that records management is very closely aligned with document control, data management and the other functions of CM.

Litigation Records Specialist	Records Management Analyst	Records Supervisor
Assist with automation of the firm's documents by way of scanning and imaging. Analyze records management problems, design corrective action strategies, assist client community to develop records management programs to include protection, database controls and customer training. Requires Master's Library Science and 3 years records management experience. E-mail resume to - - -.	Help develop and oversee administration of the City-wide records and information management program in all departments. Be responsible for developing, implementing, and maintaining policies and procedures throughout the information life cycle for business, regulatory and legal purposes. Take the lead in administering the electronic records system and become the system administrator. E-mail resume to - - -.	Supervise staff of two. Responsible for assuring the accurate management of company records. Manage projects as required. Interface with client contact to ensure satisfaction in operational objectives. Coordinate off-site storage and retrieval of files. Lifting up to 40# required. Requires previous supervision and project management experience. E-mail resume to - - -.

http://www.arma.org/careerlink/seekers/search.cfm, August 22, 2001

Table 4-2   Examples of help wanted advertisements for records management.

Document Control

The responsibilities of the *document control* function ranges from very narrow to very broad. From the most narrow point of view, the role is limited to managing assigned documents within the associated repository. This includes receiving documents into that repository, maintaining their security while they are there, and making them available to authorized individuals as needed. Such a document control clerk keeps a record of receipts, locations and issues.

At the other end of the spectrum, document control personnel may be responsible for a wide range of responsibilities per the help wanted ad provided in Table 4-3. Although the job title is described as "clerk," the list of duties represents much more than a clerical job. Most professionals associate clerical job titles with positions of relatively low pay. The listed responsibilities are important duties and include a wide range of configuration management-related tasks.

The duties probably represent what someone was doing before they left to take a better paying job. It would appear that the individual who quit, if that was the case, had extensive talent and took it upon themselves to do far more than would be expected from someone holding a clerical position. This ad appears to be an effort to find a replacement.

The Arizona Republic, Help Wanted Ads, Sunday, August 12, 2001

Document Control Clerk
Responsibilities include creating, reviewing, releasing, & controlling documents & software related to quality procedures. Additional responsibilities include recording, obtaining approval for, and changing controlled documents. Ideal candidate will be very organized, have previously worked with a document control system, specifically FDA & ISO, with a strong background in technical writing. Experience may be a substitute for education. Please FAX resume to (- - -) - - - - - - -.

Table 4-3   Example of a help wanted ad for a document control clerk.

Library Management

Most large corporations have a library and a librarian whose duties are to establish a knowledge management system for managing the firm's intellectual property for retrieval. Such property is maintained in both hardcopy and electronic format. The help wanted advertisement shown in Table 4-4 describes the typical duties of a librarian.

http://
www.flipdog.com/
js/jobdetails.html
March 27, 2002

Technical Librarian II

REQUIREMENTS:
Fully knowledgeable of library information databases such as Dialog, Lexis/Nexis, Ebsco CRN and others; resources and procedures to retrieve relevant information by searching on-line databases, DC-ROM's, Intranet, Internet etc.; various library management software; library management catalog system and Library of Congress cataloging procedures; resource services for procuring reference books, serials, and technical articles as required; engineering standards and codes, technical industry references and required library collection. Able to assist customers with electronic searches; update LAN CD-ROM jukebox bimonthly as revisions received; and index proprietary engineering documents for records retention.

MARKETING/PUBLICITY & CUSTOMER SERVICE:
Excellent oral and written communication skills; innovative and creative marketing; issuing monthly newsletter; market library services and resources to management through quarterly presentations; monthly report of services performed; assisting customers with searches and conducting customer satisfaction and management surveys.

LEADERSHIP REQUIREMENTS:
Interface to peers and service line management to meet balance scorecard plan, goals and objectives. Display positive attitude toward teamwork and collaboration; master new applications and resource services; keep up-to-date with developments in the professional information industry.

Table 4-4   Example of a help wanted advertisement for a librarian.

Organizations that focus on software development often establish a separate library that is devoted to software artifacts. All software requirements including product designs and process definition are maintained in the software library along with the products of the development effort.

The duties of a software library are similar to the combined duties of data management, document control, records management and inventory control. There are many redundancies when these functions are allowed to coexist.

Chapter 4 — Summary

CMII is configuration management, project management and quality assurance integrated into one cohesive unit. The activities of configuration management include requirements management, change management, release management, data management, records management, document control and the library function.

The four-step project management cycle of "plan, do, study and act" is two cycles, not one. The "act and plan" steps are contained in the requirements planning cycle. The "do and study" steps are contained in the physical item cycle. The requirements cycle must lead and the physical item cycle must be kept synchronized. Ability to accommodate change is a prerequisite.

Quality is properly defined as "conformance to requirements." Clear, concise and valid requirements are a prerequisite for achieving quality and also for assuring customer satisfaction. Organizations that are suffocating on corrective action all have something in common: Their requirements are out of control.

To speak the CMII language is to speak in terms of the four lowest common denominators (i.e., physical items, documents, forms and records). Each of these four common denominators are further subdivided by type.

It is necessary to lift configuration management out of its traditional engineering design orientation and give it an enterprise-wide perspective. It is necessary to expand the scope and shift the emphasis. To expand the scope is to encompass all information that could impact safety, quality, schedule, cost, profit or the environment. The emphasis must shift to continuous improvement in the ability to accommodate change and keep requirements clear, concise and valid.

To accomplish this objective, the most directly involved activities that exist throughout the organization must be brought together and integrated into one cohesive unit. The seven activities described in this chapter represent those which commonly exist.

An effort to integrate these activities under one common leader is likely to run into resistance. The proper integration will be accepted and achieved if each decision is based on a common organizational objective to "change faster and document better."

5

The CMII Model

CMII is a process for defining requirements in a manner that can be clearly communicated to, and understood by, each user.

The CMII model includes the ability to accommodate change and keep all requirements clear, concise and valid.

CM process improvement is measured by the ability to change faster and/or document better.

The appropriate business process infrastructure is a prerequisite. The CMII model provides such an infrastructure.

The previous chapters have provided insight to the myriad of safety, quality, schedule, cost and/or profitability problems that continue to plague many organizations. The previous chapters have also identified the root causes. The requirements are out of control. To eliminate those problems is to fix the requirements.

This is easier said than done since the requirements are in a constant state of change. To fix the requirements is to establish a business process infrastructure which can accommodate change and also keep the requirements clear, concise and valid.

This chapter identifies the activities most directly involved in CMII and provides a high-level schematic of the closed-loop CMII process. This chapter describes what it means to be requirements driven. It also defines the prerequisites for transitioning from the corrective action mode to the continuous improvement mode.

Business of Running a Business

Every organization, from business enterprises to government agencies, has customers. Each organization provides products and/or services to satisfy the needs of their customers. Each organization has delivery systems for producing and supporting those products and services. An organization that wishes to stay in business must continually improve its products, services and delivery systems.

The competitive strength of an organization is derived from its delivery systems. Every organization must match the needs of its customers with the capabilities of their delivery systems. Its products and services, as shown in Figure 5-1, are a tradeoff between what its customers need and what its delivery systems can do.

The customer's needs are a moving target. That is why organizations strive to be lean and agile. Lean implies reliable and efficient. Agile implies ability to change quickly without compromising reliability or efficiency. To consider configuration management an asset, rather than a handicap, is a paradigm shift.

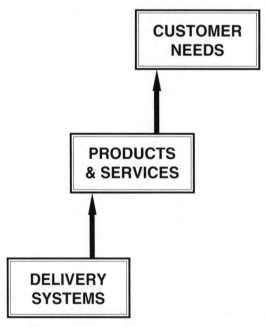

Figure 5-1   Products and services: a trade-off between needs and capabilities.

What it Means to Be Requirements-Driven

Once an organization establishes the needs of its customers in the form of released documents, those needs are treated as requirements. The same is true for each product and/or service provided to satisfy those customer needs. The same is also true for the delivery systems for those products and services, as shown in Figure 5-2.

All organizational activity is thereby driven by requirements. The results of each action must conform to the specific requirement. This approach is compatible with the ISO 9000 quality standards wherein organizations must "document what they do and do what they document." A complementary CMII rule is that a requirement is not a requirement until it is documented and released. This is what it means to be requirements-driven.

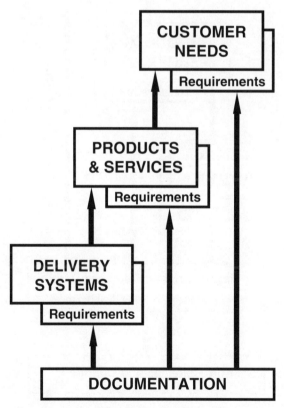

Figure 5-2   A requirements-driven organization works to released documents.

Scope and Emphasis of CMII

Figure 5-3 helps to show why change management is the backbone of requirements management. All three sets of requirements are in a continual state of change. Updates must be quick and synchronization must be maintained. Consistent conformance becomes a byproduct when requirements are clear, concise and valid. This applies to all three sets of requirements.

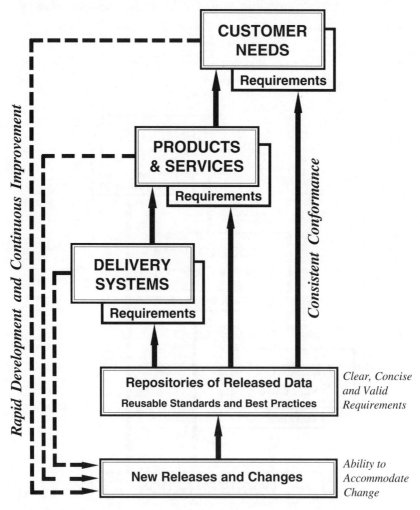

Figure 5-3   Overall scope and emphasis of CMII.

Corrective Action Versus Continuous Improvement

Each corrective action is a symptom of deficiencies in the requirements. Requirements cannot be kept clear, concise and valid when the change process is slow and cumbersome. There is no time for continuous improvement when resources are being consumed with corrective action.

Any organization that operates in the corrective action mode is placing its survival at risk. To escape that mode requires doing whatever it takes to assure that requirements are clear, concise and valid and to maintain their integrity as they change. Resources spent on corrective action may then shift to real improvements.

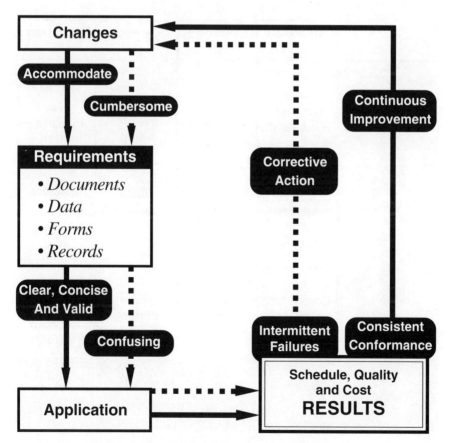

Figure 5-4   Corrective action and root causes.

Prerequisites for Eliminating Corrective Action

Figure 5-5 describes four situations and how each influences quality of life. The differences are a function of requirements and conformance measurements. The integrity in each case may range from good to poor and the results that can be expected with each combination are provided.

Quality of life is best when operating in Situation 1. Situation 4 is the most undesirable place to be. It is also a difficult place to escape. The situation in which an organization operates is dictated by its delivery systems. An organization that operates anywhere other than Situation 1 needs to improve its delivery systems.

	Situation 1	Situation 2	Situation 3	Situation 4
Integrity of Documented Requirements	Clear, Concise And Valid	Clear, Concise And Valid	Subject To Interpretation	Subject To Interpretation
Integrity of Conformance Measurements	Easily Applied And Concise	Subject To Interpretation	Easily Applied And Concise	Subject To Interpretation
Results	Consistent Conformance	Inter-mittent Errors	Inter-mittent Errors	Working harder to stay even (chaos)
Quality of Life	Organized and Improving	Corrective Action Mode	Corrective Action Mode	Frustration and Finger Pointing

Figure 5-5   Factors which influence quality of life in the work place.

Intervention Resources and Their Magnitude

Intervention resources are the resources spent on corrective action as needed to rescue quality and schedule. The magnitude of those resources can be measured but accurate measurements are rare. Most are understated. Commonly missed costs include the following:
- effort to find needed documents;
- interpretation of the requirements;
- meetings to discuss the requirements;
- creation of missing documents;
- correction of existing documents;
- expediting of missing ingredients.

This list does not include the effort spent reworking physical items to make them acceptable for use. Statistics compiled by the Institute of Configuration Management reveal that most organizations spend 40 to 60% of their resources on intervention.

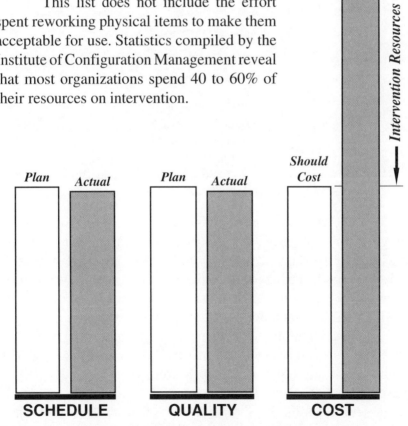

Figure 5-6   Intervention resources used to rescue quality and schedule.

CMII and the Functional Activities Involved

The basis for CMII and the CMII objectives were initially described on page 21. The range of functional activities needed to accomplish those objectives were identified on page 35. Figure 5-7 serves to illustrate how the seven activities of configuration management interface with project management and quality assurance.

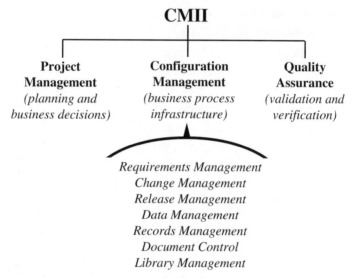

CMII

| **Project Management** | **Configuration Management** | **Quality Assurance** |
| *(planning and business decisions)* | *(business process infrastructure)* | *(validation and verification)* |

Requirements Management
Change Management
Release Management
Data Management
Records Management
Document Control
Library Management

Figure 5-7   Configuration management activities under one umbrella.

The CMII model represents a standardized methodology for applying project management, configuration management and quality assurance to each and every project. It does not matter whether a project is a product or a process, new development or a modification, hardware or software, large or small, simple or complex. The activities and the methodology are the same in each case.

The configuration management component, in its reinvented state, is the key ingredient that makes CMII what it is. The CM component is what sets CMII apart from other business process improvement initiatives. The reinvented CM component provides the infrastructure that has been missing. It is that infrastructure which enables project management and quality assurance to be effective.

Functional Schematic of the CMII Process

A high-level, functional schematic of the CMII process is provided in Figure 5-8. It is a change-friendly process. The ability to accommodate change is enabled by how requirements are identified, structured, linked and owned. Those same considerations also enable the methods for validating the requirements to be effective.

The overall CMII process includes the ability to communicate the requirements to each user in a manner that is prompt and precise. Any loss in clarity is to be avoided.

Reliable and efficient conformance measurements are also part of the closed-loop process. The cycle is driven by continuous improvement and consistent conformance is a byproduct.

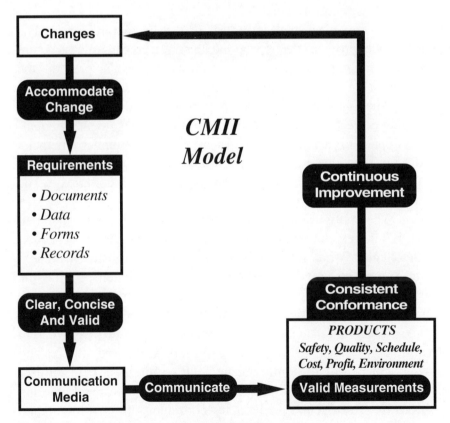

Figure 5-8   Functional schematic of the CMII model.

Chapter 5 — Summary

The CMII model is an integration of project management, configuration management and quality assurance. Contributions of project management include project planning and business decisions. Contributions of quality assurance include validation of requirements and verification that physical items conform. Configuration management contributes by providing the business process infrastructure upon which project management and quality assurance can perform their duties reliably and efficiently.

The competitive strength of an organization is derived from its delivery systems. Every organization must match the needs of its customers with the capabilities of its delivery systems. Its products and services are a trade-off between what its customers need and what its delivery systems can do.

All organizational activity is driven by requirements. The CMII model provides the appropriate business process infrastructure for managing requirements. Such an infrastructure also provides the foundation for an organization's delivery systems.

The CMII model represents a standardized methodology for applying project management, configuration management and quality assurance to each and every project. It does not matter whether a project is a product or a process, new development or a modification, hardware or software, large or small, simple or complex. The activities and the methodology are the same in each case.

The configuration management component in its reinvented state is the key ingredient that makes CMII what it is. The CM component is what sets CMII apart from other business process improvement initiatives. The reinvented CM component provides the infrastructure that has been missing. It is that infrastructure which enables project management and quality assurance to be effective.

CMII is a change-friendly process. It is a process wherein requirements must be properly identified, structured, linked and owned. It is able to communicate each requirement to each user promptly and precisely. Conformance measurements are reliable and efficient. The cycle is driven by continuous improvement and consistent conformance is a byproduct.

6

Product Structuring and Baselines

*Each end-item product represents a hierarchy of
physical items that have specific parent-to-child relationships.*

*Properly structured physical item hierarchies provide the
ideal framework for as-planned and as-released baselines.*

*Each item residing at each level has its own unique
set of design and process-related documentation.*

*Each like-family of end-items (or model) should have its
own as-planned and as-released baseline.*

A configuration can be any type of entity. It can be a product, a facility or a business enterprise. The hierarchy of a configuration can range from a facility to a furnace to a pipe, from a building to a wall to a nail, from an automobile to a wheel to a tire, from a computer to a software program to a source code file, from a book to its cover to a sheet of paper, from a business enterprise to a strategic business plan to a procedure.

To create the appropriate hierarchy requires logic and the needs of all parties must be understood. There are no widely accepted industry standards. Those who work in different life cycle phases have different preferences. This chapter serves to identify preferred practices and rules. It describes how to provide the appropriate linkages and use such hierarchies as the framework for as-planned and as-released baselines.

Bills of Material and Parent-to-Child Relationships

New products are generally not totally new. They often represent a new application for an existing product. They often represent repackaged versions of existing products. They often represent different combinations of existing components. New products may not even contain a single component that is totally new.

A business enterprise competes by minimizing the time and cost required to bring new products to market. Styling may be new, components may be arranged differently, packaging may be different and performance may be improved. Basic components, however, are rarely new. Most new products represent a reuse of existing and proven components. Organizations that are best at such reuse have a tremendous advantage.

A *bill of material* is another name for a *parts list*. It could be a listing of components contained in an assembly. It could be a listing of ingredients used to make a cake. It could be a listing of source code files used to compile a software program. It could be a listing of raw materials used to make a tire. A bill of material is a document. It is only one of several types of documents.

An end-item product may contain any number of assemblies and components. Each assembly may be subdivided into subassemblies and components. Each subassembly contains components. The bills of material for two or more end-item configurations could be identical except for one or two assemblies and/or components.

Product structuring is the process of breaking an end-item configuration down into its hierarchy of assemblies, modules, components and/or raw materials. The structure must include consideration for how the product is designed, how it is to be built, how it is to be operated and how it is to be supported and maintained. It includes consideration for customer-selected options and how they should be organized within the overall hierarchy.

The preferences for how a product should be structured will differ by life-cycle phase. The various activities must work together and identify the structure that can best satisfy everyone's needs. The same end-item product may have multiple hierarchies. Ability to keep those hierarchies synchronized is an important consideration.

System Schematics and Interface Definition

The parent-to-child relationships as provided by bills of material represent only one of several important relationships. The component contained in an end-item product may have a variety of relationships with other components. Functional schematics are used to define functional relationships between physical items. Interface documents are also used to define both physical and functional relationships between specific items.

A complex product such as an automobile may utilize several functional schematics. For example, the electrical system, the fuel system, the start system and the brake system may each have their own functional schematic. The same functional component, such as the starter motor, may reside in more than one functional schematic.

Maintenance personnel commonly use functional schematics when troubleshooting a complex product. Mechanics who work with the same product for long periods of time generally have the schematics memorized. They might refer to a schematic if they run into a problem that they have not experienced before.

Interface documents exist in a variety of formats and are often referred to by other names. An example of an interface document might be one that defines the interface between an electrical plug and its receptacle. Another example might be one that defines the signal between a television set and its remote control device. The installation drawings that were described on page 2 represent another example of interface drawings.

The point of all this boils down to determining how this important information should be organized and integrated with the overall physical item hierarchy. How such information is identified and linked becomes especially important when making changes and trying to keep all information sets properly synchronized.

A functional schematic should be linked to the physical item that contains all the functional items contained in that schematic. For example, if a hauling system is comprised of a tractor and a wagon and all components contained in the schematic reside in the wagon, the schematic is linked to the wagon. Interface documents are linked to the level that contains both interfacing components.

End-Item Application Requirements

It is important to make a distinction between what an end-item product must do versus what it can do. An automobile, for example, must comply with the environmental regulations that exist in the country or state where it is to be sold and driven. Such regulations may differ from country to country and from state to state. Such regulations represent application requirements. An automobile producer must determine how to ensure its product conforms to these regulations and all other application requirements.

The physical item hierarchy provides an effective way to bring proper visibility to the full spectrum of application requirements. The end-item product, which normally represents the uppermost level of a physical item hierarchy, is lowered one notch. An extra box is placed above the end-item product. All application requirements are linked to the higher-level box.

The indenture levels within a physical item hierarchy are often numbered. Automated scheduling systems, for example, often treat the end-item as "level 1." The next level down within the physical item hierarchy is "level 2" and so on. To retain this convention, it is appropriate to identify the application requirements as "level 0."

The application requirements which reside at level 0 represent what the end-item product must do. The design information that defines the end-item product and what it can do is linked directly to the end-item itself, which resides at level 1. Proper separation between what a product must do and what it can do is very important.

This importance becomes increasingly apparent during product development. The first two steps of the eight-step development process, as discussed in Chapter 10, serve to define (1) the application requirements and (2) the basis for detailed design. It was very apparent in some of the failures discussed in Chapter 3 that one or both of these first two steps were skipped.

Any organization that wants to get its arms around its requirements must start at the top. The first two steps of development are the most important steps of all even though they are relatively brief. These first two steps, if conducted properly, consume less than six percent of the total development effort.

Document Types and User-Friendly Formats

The CMII model is not necessarily physical item centric or document centric. It could be called physical item centric since physical item hierarchies are used as the framework for as-planned and as-released baselines and each item residing at each level is linked to it own unique set of supporting documents.

The model could just as accurately be considered document centric since bills of material are used to define the physical item hierarchy and bills of material are documents. The fact that so much emphasis is placed on documentation also supports this classification.

The more important point is that both physical items and documents represent lowest common denominators. Both are further subdivided by type. Documents within the CMII methodology are identified by type, number and revision level.

Any organization striving to improve its business processes must eventually identify the types of documents that are to be used to run the business. Design-oriented information should not be mixed with process-oriented information. Parts lists should not be mixed with illustrations. A medium-sized organization might have as many as 10 types of design-oriented documents and that many more process-oriented documents. Enterprise operating standards represent a specific type of document and their supporting administrative procedures represent another type. Process standards, such as how to submit a change request, represent additional document types.

Each type of document is preferably limited to a specific type of information. Overall effectiveness of a document is compromised when it contains too much information or different types of information. For example, different designs should not be provided on the same document and design definition should not be mixed with process definition. Such limitations may represent a major paradigm shift for some organizations.

The format for each type of document should be standardized. Consistency in the format makes it easier to understand its content. The best format is that which best serves the needs of its users. The best format is also change friendly. Visibility of how a document has changed should be readily available.

Primary Versus Secondary Items and Documents

The physical items that reside in a physical item hierarchy used as the framework for an as-planned and as-released baseline are referred to as *primary items*. Primary items are the assemblies and components contained in an as-built product or facility. The tools and equipment used to develop, produce and support those primary items are referred to as *secondary items*.

Supporting documents that are linked directly to primary items are referred to as *primary documents*. There are two types of *secondary documents*. A document that supports a secondary item is a secondary document. A document that describes how to perform a repetitive process (or standard process) represents the second type of secondary document.

Since everything is in a continual state of change, the manner in which primary items, primary documents, secondary items and secondary documents are linked become important considerations. Secondary items are linked to primary process documents, which describe how they are to be applied to primary items. Secondary items are not linked directly to primary items.

Documents that define standard processes are also linked to the primary process documents, which specify the step at which they are to be used. Standard process documents are not linked directly to primary items. The linkages of secondary items and documents to primary process documents are accomplished in a manner whereby a change to one does not automatically force the other to change.

Secondary items and documents are generally outside the scope of traditional approaches to configuration management. That is another area in which that scope has been expanded. That is where the cost of change often has the greatest impact. The impact a change has on secondary items should not be something that is discovered during its implementation phase.

It should be possible to perform a where-used inquiry on any primary item and identify all its active applications. It should be similarly possible to perform a where-used inquiry on any secondary item or standardized process and identify all active applications. The appropriate linkages make this possible.

As-Planned and As-Released Baselines

The framework for an as-planned and as-released baseline is provided by the physical item hierarchy for the associated product. A baseline is initiated with the enterprise change notice that releases the first definitive document in the earliest phase of development. It may be nothing more than a concept document. The baseline continues to evolve as the concept evolves into more detail and as additional items and documents are identified. The baseline ratchets forward with the additional information provided by each enterprise change notice.

The earliest version of such a baseline contains everything that is known about what the product is going to be. That portion of the baseline represents its as-planned state. The development of such a baseline is equivalent to the development of a tree. The main trunk and major branches may be known but many of the smaller limbs and leaves have yet to be defined.

Branches and limbs are equivalent to physical items. Leaves are equivalent to documents. Branches and/or limbs that already exist, and which are to be reused, are added to the evolving baseline as soon as they are identified. Their existing leaves come with them. That portion of the baseline represents its as-released state.

Each as-planned document has an as-planned release date. Once released, its release date is recorded. The baseline is not the place to keep track of actual release dates relative to planned dates. As-planned release dates, however, must be kept up-to-date. Such a baseline is a working repository of valuable information and the highest degree of clarity and integrity must be maintained.

As stated previously, the as-planned and as-released baseline is a moving baseline. To add, delete or change a physical item requires that a bill of material be changed. To add, delete or change any item or document requires that the baseline be updated.

Superseded and superseding items and documents are displayed along with their effectivities. The effectivity specifies when to transition from one to the other. Each change has an effectivity. Each document has an effective date. Physical items and documents are moved from the active baseline to a history file once they have been superseded and are no longer part of the current configuration.

Enhanced Approach to Concurrent Engineering

Products are often designed without a lot of consideration for how they will be built or maintained. Many approaches have been used to get downstream disciplines to participate in the development effort and assure that their needs are not overlooked. That is why the U.S. Department of Defense began emphasizing total life cycle costs (rather than development costs alone) when awarding contracts for the development of new weapon systems.

Concurrent engineering was formally introduced in 1989 for a similar purpose. Concurrent engineering is an approach wherein the development effort is accomplished by a cross-functional team whose members represent each life cycle phase. Such representation is a step in the right direction but other issues had to be addressed. Should such participation be voluntary? Should it be a part-time effort for some and a full-time effort for others?

As organizations struggled with these issues, it became apparent that the underlying objective was to improve communications between the development team members. The obvious way to do that was to bring them together in the same room located in the proximity of the development site. It was also concluded that there should be no walled offices or doors in the office area. It would seem that the opportunity for team members to interface and communicate had been optimized.

Although all team members were now in the same location near the development site, success was still not assured. Much of the success was still being derived from individual heroics. The development status was changing daily. It was still difficult to see all the pieces of the puzzle. There were a lot of changes. There was a lot of planning and replanning. There had to be a better way to keep track of what had been accomplished, what remained to be done and how the new plan differed from the previous plan.

An as-planned and as-released baseline provides such visibility. It is the central source for information. All parties contribute to the information and all parties are users. It makes little difference where the team members are located. Each member can see the total picture. All parties are driven by one common set of priorities.

Fallacies of Learning Curves

The learning curve was adapted from the historical observation that individuals who perform repetitive tasks exhibit an improvement in performance as the task is repeated a number of times. Learning curves are sometimes called experience curves. The cost of producing the tenth unit will be less than the cost of producing the first unit. Per unit costs will decrease as volume increases.

Such curves would be hyperbolic if plotted on graph paper with regular coordinates since the decline in unit costs is not constant. Experience has shown that there is a constant percentage reduction in time required over successfully doubled quantities of units produced. This type of decline, if plotted on a logarithmic scale, results in a straight line. The slope of the line represents the rate of learning and is used to project future costs. The straight line is easy to work with. The point to be negotiated is the slope of the line, or rate of learning.

Extensive surveys and tests have shown that learning curves for a wide variety of products run in the neighborhood of 80%. This means that the hours between doubled quantities are reduced by 20%. (Hours to build the 8th unit will be 20% less than the 4th unit, the 100th will be 20% less than the 50th, and so on).

Learning curves were traditionally used in defense contracts. Such contracts were typically awarded for a specific quantity in a specific period and extended on a period-by-period basis as needed. Such curves provided a way for contracting agencies and contractors to agree on pricing for each extension.

It is important to note that the slope of the curve must include consideration for engineering changes and the associated relearning that must take place with each change. The slope is influenced by the stability of the configuration and the impact of changes.

Second, many learning curve studies were based on building to print rather than step-by-step process plans. Learning curves in a job shop environment are highly influenced by the quality of the process definition. They tend to flatten out as the process definition improves. The curve can stay relatively flat with changes, provided the process definition remains clear, concise and valid. As process definition improves, the need for learning curves declines.

Information Repositories

Repositories for storing various types of information are also an important part of the overall business process infrastructure. Automation and the transition to a paperless environment have had a tremendous impact on how information is stored and retrieved. It is appropriate to restate the requirements to be achieved by those systems which, in themselves, have not changed. It is the tools and methods that have changed.

A repository is a place to put information where it will be safe and where the security is in accordance with its level of importance. The information that resides in a repository, however, is not static. It is in a continual state of change. Information is continually added and/or deleted and/or changed. Placement of information in a repository should not restrict the ability for authorized individuals to gain access and make changes as needed.

Engineers are well known for their reluctance to release any documents for which they are responsible. Whether finished or not, they know that changes will be forthcoming. They also know how difficult it can be to change a document after it has been released. Document users have a similar challenge. They may know that a document is incorrect but feel it is too difficult to get it changed. Users may choose to keep marked-up copies rather than wrestle with the slow and cumbersome change process.

Some organizations also have trouble finding information. Some never bothered to place released information in a secure area. Some never bothered to take the documents away from the engineers. Some never bothered to identify the various information sets in a manner wherein they could be filed in a logical manner. Some never got around to replacing the cardboard boxes that have been used as storage files since the company was formed.

An organization must take care of its information like banks take care of money. Just as each penny is important to a bank, each bit of information that could impact safety, quality, schedule, cost, profit or the environment should be important to a business enterprise. The appropriate tools and methods will be forthcoming once the requirements are clearly stated and enforced.

Baseline for the Business Enterprise

A business enterprise represents a configuration in itself. It has its own hierarchy of documented requirements. Such a hierarchy is made up of administrative requirements rather than physical item requirements. An as-planned and as-released baseline for the business enterprise would include the hierarchy of administrative requirements as shown in Table 6-1.

- *Business regulations*
- *Mission statement*
- *Strategic business plan (high-level plan)*
- *Organizational policies*
- *Operating plan (day-to-day)*
- *Core business processes (basis for detailed plan)*
- *Enterprise operating standards (detailed plan)*
- *Enabling tools*
- *Supporting procedures*

Table 6-1   Hierarchy of administrative requirements for a business enterprise.

There is a general consensus that a business enterprise should organize around its core business processes but there has never been an accepted standard for how that should be done. Table 6-1 provides a template for how that should be done. The enterprise operating standards represent a consolidated set of the requirements that each core business process must accomplish. The traditional quality manual, as it exists today, would be superseded by such standards.

The administrative procedures are used in conjunction with enabling tools to achieve the operating standards. The operating standards are designed to accomplish the requirements of the various business programs in a manner that is reliable and efficient.

An organizational chart provides the appropriate framework for an as-planned and as-released baseline for a business enterprise, just as a physical item hierarchy provides the appropriate framework for an as-planned and as-released baseline for a product.

Chapter 6 — Summary

Product structuring is the process of breaking an end-item configuration down into its hierarchy of assemblies, modules, components and/or raw materials. The structure must include consideration for how the product is to be designed, built, operated, supported and maintained. It includes consideration for customer-selected options and how they are to be integrated into the overall hierarchy.

The preferences for how a product should be structured will differ by life cycle phase. The various activities must work together and identify the structure that can best satisfy everyone's needs. The same end-item product may have multiple hierarchies. Ability to keep those hierarchies synchronized as changes take place is an important consideration.

Product structuring includes consideration for how physical items are linked to each other and to their supporting documentation. Bills of material are used to define the parent-to-child relationships between physical items. Each item residing at each level in the hierarchy is linked to its own unique set of supporting documents. Each document is identified by type, number and revision level.

The uppermost level of the physical item hierarchy is designated as "level 0." End-item application requirements are linked to a placeholder above the end-item, which is designated as level 0. Documents that provide the basis for detailed design are linked directly to the end-item, which resides at level 1.

Physical items and documents are segregated into primary and secondary categories. Primary items and documents are those that represent the product. Secondary items and documents are comprised of equipment, tools and standard processes. Appropriate linkages make it possible to perform an inquiry on any item or document and identify all applications.

Any organization striving to improve its business processes must eventually identify the types of documents to be used to run the business. Documents are identified by type, number and revision level and formats are standardized for each type. Each document is preferably limited to a specific type of information. The best format is that which best serves the needs of its users.

7
Changes, Forms and Effectivities

The only constant is change. Nothing remains static forever.

Each improvement and each corrective action is a change.

Change forms are used as templates to guide work through the change process in a manner that is reliable and efficient.

Change effectivities are used to control the transition from superseded requirements to superseding requirements.

Interchangeability, traceability and effectivity are key words.

Most organizations use multiple change processes to maintain the various repositories of released information. A change to one information set is likely to trigger changes to other sets. In the absence of proper linkages and integration, impacted information is often overlooked. In the absence of speed and efficiency, there is no certainty that requirements will lead and physical items will follow. If this is not the case, information integrity is certain to erode.

The goal is to standardize one reliable and efficient change process that can satisfy the needs of all parties. Such a process is closed-loop and revolves around as-planned and as-released baselines, which are closely coupled with the various repositories of released information and records. This chapter describes some of the key elements of such a change process.

Relationships of Lowest Common Denominators

The "engineering change process" is undoubtedly more complex than any other process used by an organization. The change process will never be simple but it can, nevertheless, be simplified. This is where the importance of the appropriate common denominators becomes clear. Their proper relationships are as shown in Figure 7-1.

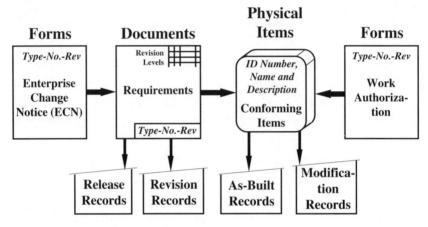

Figure 7-1   Relationships between forms, documents, items and records.

Changes are written against documents, not physical items. The enterprise change notice (ECN) form provides the authority for releasing and changing documents. Physical items must conform to their requirements.

All work that is accomplished is recorded and retained. There is a release record for each released document. There is a revision record for each document that is revised. There is an as-built record for each physical item that is produced. There is a modification record for each physical item that is modified.

Records are comprised of completed forms and referenced documents. The forms that authorize work include reference to the requirements to which the results must conform. Records include evidence that the results of the completed work did, in fact, conform to the requirements.

Rules of Interchangeability

The rules of interchangeability apply to physical items. Those that are fully interchangeable should have the same internally assigned identification number. This means that such items may be placed in the same inventory bin or library location and used interchangeably in any application, regardless of the revision levels of the associated documents to which they conform. Many individuals will find this to be a scary idea and would never consider trying to follow such rules (even though they are deeply mired in corrective action).

Conversely, physical items which are not fully interchangeable cannot be allowed to have the same internally assigned identification number. Many organizations break this rule. They do so by making noninterchangeable changes to the product and allowing the identification number to remain unchanged. If they do update the documentation, they simply advance its revision level. Such a practice is typical of those who are most deeply mired in corrective action.

Most organizations want to follow the right rules but have difficulty in doing so. Strict enforcement of the rules of identification and reidentification are difficult because of the time and effort required to revise identification numbers and upgrade the associated documentation. The costs are dependent upon how items and documents are identified and linked in addition to the efficiency of the change process.

Every organization has taken a run at improving its change process. Most of those efforts bog down and actual improvements are minimal. Every organization has also taken one or more runs at finding ways to make noninterchangeable changes and retain control without changing identification numbers. One set of problems is simply traded for another set.

Many organizations try to solve these deeply rooted problems with automation, but it is essentially impossible to transform a bad process into a good process with automation alone. Ability to bring documentation on-line does not necessarily mean that on-line documentation can be maintained. It is often discovered that the change process and the functionality of enabling tools are both deficient.

Traceability of Changes to Specific End-Items

Companies in the business of producing products are often required to know the exact content of each and every end-item configuration they ship to their customers. Companies that produce medical devices are one example. Their products and processes must conform to the regulations provided by the U.S. Food and Drug Administration.

The fact that such products are tested and verified to conform to each and every physical and functional requirement is not good enough. Companies must also be able to prove that they know the specific changes contained in each end-item and how each one differs from the others. This is true whether a change caused items to be reidentified or not. They must also be able to prove that the processes used to produce those products are properly managed.

Such traceability requirements represent a major challenge, even when the products being produced are small and relatively simple. The challenge becomes far greater when end-item products are large and highly complex. Although the extensive complexity cannot be sorted out at this time, one point is very clear. An organization must retain positive control of everything it does.

There are certain rules that can help to ensure that the regulated requirements are achieved while also minimizing the costs. The rules of interchangeability must be clear and they must be followed. A work authorization to produce a physical item must reference the specific design document that the item must conform to. The work authorization must also reference the specific process document that is used to produce that product. The completed work authorization must be retained as part of the as-built records.

Changes that impact the design of the product, or the processes used to produce that product, should be grouped together in accordance with their impact and their priority and implemented as one change. Reidentification can thereby be based on interchangeability and not be overly influenced by traceability requirements.

Serialization may also play a key role in how end-item traceability is achieved. This subject is discussed on the following page and is often referred to as *lot traceability*.

Lot Traceability

Lot controlled items are identified by their identification number and name plus lot number and serial number (if they have a serial number). Lot traceability extends the identification routines for physical items to include lot numbers and serial numbers and ensures that each procured lot is homogeneous.

A homogeneous lot is one in which all members are produced during the same process and each subordinate-level material is also from a homogeneous lot. If the members of a lot are produced in more than one run of the same process, those members are not homogeneous. If the subordinate-level materials used to produce a lot of the parent-level item are not homogeneous themselves, then the members of the parent-level lot are not homogeneous.

Lot traceability may be one-way or two-way. One-way means that the source for each and every physical item that has been received into inventory is known. Each of those items or materials can be traced back to their source lot. The supplier from which each lot was obtained is also recorded and retained in history. Two-way traceability means that both the source and the current location for each member of each lot are known.

Lot control procedures are applied to an item when the potential benefits outweigh the added costs. The major benefit is improved ability to contain the costs of a health, safety or quality issue that could occur as a result of using the item. The issue revolves around undetectable differences that may exist in items that are supposedly identical. Such undetectable differences are more likely to occur in items from different lots than items from the same lot. If one item from a lot is found to have a defect, other items from the same lot are likely to have the same defect.

Some items can be serialized while others do not lend themselves to serialization. It is often possible to serialize the container when the item cannot be serialized. In any case, lot controlled items always have a lot number. They may or may not have a serial number.

In the case where all physical items within an end-item product are subjected to two-way lot traceability, the requirements for end-item traceability are also met.

Change Forms and Formats

The change process can be no better than the forms being used to manage that process. The importance of good forms cannot be overstated, yet they tend to remain underdeveloped. They will remain underdeveloped until all parties can agree on how the change process should work. The appropriate forms can then be developed accordingly. Forms are simply templates for guiding work through that process.

The tendency to cram all information into a single, multi-page form must be avoided for the same reason that all design and process-related information for a physical item should not be established and maintained in the same multi-page document. Such documents are not user-friendly. Such forms are not user-friendly.

Each change form must serve a specific purpose. Single-page forms are best. Appropriate forms are derived by dividing the high-level change process into standardized subprocesses. Each subprocess should have the same start point and the same end point. The steps between the start and end points should be repetitive. The form should emulate those steps. The form should make the process steps intuitive.

Each subprocess within a higher-level process is a candidate to have its own form. The transition from one subprocess and its form to the next subprocess and the next form must be clear and crisp. The first form will often become a supplement to the next form. Automation does not eliminate the need for good forms.

Forms are used to define problems and proposed solutions. They are used to provide cost estimates and to record business decisions. They are used to plan the implementation of approved changes. They provide a record of all change-related work that was accomplished and the basis for that work.

The change process within the CMII model utilizes four basic forms. Two are used in the analysis phase and two others are used in the implementation phase. Each form represents a one-page format. Attachments are added as appropriate.

Form for Deviations and Waivers

Any physical item that is to be accepted in a noncon-forming state must be authorized and a record of such an acceptance must be retained. A "deviation or waiver" form is used for this purpose. The form is used as a *deviation* if the nonconforming condition was expected before the work was initiated. The form is used as a *waiver* if the nonconforming condition was not expected. It is the same form in either case.

The deviation/waiver form is not part of the change process. It is used by the downstream activities that perform work on physical items. The identification number and name of the nonconforming physical item are recorded on the form along with the work authorization number and date. The "as-is versus as-should-be" conditions are recorded on the form along with the quantity of items that share that nonconforming condition. The completed form is retained with the as-built records and a copy may accompany the nonconforming items.

The reason that the item is being accepted in its noncon-forming condition is also recorded on the form. Organizations that experience a lot of nonconformances often use standard-ized codes for such explanation purposes.

Deviations become popular when it takes less effort to get approval for a nonconformance than it takes to change (and correct) a requirement. Some organizations are so accustomed to writing deviations and waivers that they cannot imagine working in an environment where they do not exist. Some organizations try to force a resolution by limiting the number of deviations that can be written for the same problem.

Waivers are written after the incident to cover un-planned mistakes. Those who are accustomed to writing deviations and/or waivers have the mindset that products do not have to conform. They are forced to adopt a position that acceptable-for-use is good enough. They more than likely did not have that mindset when they started their job. It is some-thing they gained after learning how difficult it is to fix the requirements. It is easier to write a deviation or a waiver.

Change Effectivities and Controlling Documents

Change effectivities are a very complex subject. There are many ways to assign effectivities. An effectivity generally serves to specify when a change will become effective within a product and/or a process. It also serves to specify when something may be used in place of something else. It serves to specify when one set of requirements is to be superseded by another set of requirements.

Within the CMII methodology, change effectivities are specified on the enterprise change notice (ECN) form. The same form includes an impact matrix wherein all primary items and primary documents impacted by the change are identified. The impact of a change may range from a single document to a hierarchy of physical items and their associated documents. The as-planned and as-released baselines provide the mechanism for implementing the effectivity as specified on each ECN form.

All information contained in an as-planned and as-released baseline is derived from the ECN form. The ECN-specified effectivity is linked to the highest-level documents within the baseline that are impacted by that specific change. Those highest-level documents thereby become the "controlling documents" for that ECN.

If an ECN impacts a hierarchy of physical items and documents, the controlling documents are those which are linked to the highest level item within that hierarchy. Since the requirements at the subordinate levels are driven by the controlling documents, it is not necessary to assign effectivities to the subordinate-level documents. An ECN may have multiple effectivities if the change impacts multiple baselines and if the effectivity cannot be the same for each baseline.

A baseline ratchets forward with each ECN. All new and superseding documents carry the ECN's identification number. The impact matrix for each ECN also represents a "was-is" record for each update to the baseline. It is possible to retrieve a complete history of each baseline if needed.

Reschedules and Effectivity Maintenance

One of the biggest challenges associated with effectivities is their maintenance. The process of implementing a single change may involve a wide variety of tasks. Those tasks usually have many interdependencies. An effectivity is derived from the planned completion dates for the tasks required to implement the change. An effectivity is only as good as the integrity of the implementation plan from which it was derived.

Change effectivities, once assigned, cannot be ignored. Effectivity maintenance is a significant part of the change management process. Effectivities have to be monitored and adjusted as situations change. Adjustments, when needed, must be timely.

Very few organizations are fully satisfied with how they currently assign and maintain change effectivities. Most organizations continue to search for a better way. One part of the solution is to minimize the number of effectivities that have to be assigned and maintained. Another is to establish a reliable and efficient way to handle those that must be assigned and maintained.

The need for changes can not be eliminated, but some methods for implementing changes are certainly better than others. Effectivities are generally needed when a subordinate-level item is changed and its parent-level item is not reidentified. More specifically, effectivities are needed when a subordinate-level item is changed and the parent-level item used in the build schedule is not reidentified. If the physical item used in the build schedule is reidentified, an effectivity is not needed.

There is a high degree of dependency between changes to configurations and changes to build schedules. The effectivities for most changes are based on current build schedules. A change to a build schedule may disrupt any number of assigned effectivities. Consequently, changes to build schedules must be controlled in the same manner that changes to configurations are controlled. An impact analysis must be conducted with each proposed change to the build schedule.

Chapter 7 — Summary

The goal is to standardize one common change process that is sufficiently reliable and efficient to satisfy the needs of all parties. Such a process is closed-loop and revolves around as-planned and as-released baselines, which are closely coupled with the various repositories of released information and records.

The change process will never be simple but it can, nevertheless, be simplified. Most organizations want to follow the right rules but have difficulty in doing so. The appropriate common denominators must be established first. This must be followed by rules for how interchangeability, end-item traceability and effectivities are to be achieved.

The change process can be no better than the forms being used to manage that process. The importance of good forms cannot be overstated, yet they tend to remain underdeveloped. They will remain underdeveloped until all parties can agree on how the change process should work. The appropriate forms can then be developed accordingly. Forms are simply templates for guiding work through that process.

The deviation/waiver form is not part of the change process. Deviations serve to define a planned and approved nonconformance. Waivers serve to gain approval for an unplanned nonconformance. Deviations and waivers become popular when less effort is needed to get approval for a nonconformance than it takes to correct a requirement.

Change effectivities serve to specify the point at which one set of requirements is to be superseded by another set. Within the CMII methodology, change effectivities are specified on the ECN form. The same form includes an impact matrix wherein all primary items and primary documents impacted by the change are identified.

The number of assigned change effectivities can be minimized. Those that are assigned cannot be ignored. Assigned effectivities have to be monitored and adjusted in a timely manner as situations change. Effectivity maintenance is a significant part of the change management process.

8
Naming and Numbering Conventions

Identification numbers are used to control the application of physical items and their interchangeability.

Physical items that have the same identification number are, by definition, fully interchangeable.

Significant numbers are acceptable in certain applications.

Each physical item is formally named and described.

Documents are identified by type, number and revision level.

An organization's ability to manage its configurations is enhanced by the strengths, or compromised by the weaknesses, of its naming and numbering conventions. The best numbering convention is that which can best control application and interchangeability and also support reidentification. The best naming convention is that which can best identify similarities and differences between physical items and thereby support their reuse.

There are no widely accepted standards for either naming or numbering. Numbering is a very controversial subject for which no authoritative books have been published. Most articles that have been written focus on the negatives of using significant numbers (wherein the digits have meaning). This chapter provides recommended guidelines for naming and numbering which support the CMII objectives.

ID Numbers for Positive Control of Applications

To understand an effective way to achieve positive control of physical item applications is to understand how bills of material are used. As discussed in chapter 6, a bill of material serves to identify the parent-to-child relationships between physical items. If an assembly, for example, is comprised of 10 components, the bill of material for that assembly identifies those 10 components.

A bill of material includes four basic elements of information for each physical item that is listed. Those four basic elements are the identification number, name, quantity and unit of measure. The key element is the identification number. The name simply follows along with the identification number. Anytime the number appears, the name is also displayed.

Positive control of physical item applications can be assured to the degree that identification numbers can be trusted. Identification numbers can be trusted to the degree that the rules of interchangeability and reidentification are being followed when changes are made. This is often a major issue. This is why some organizations assign revision levels to their physical items and include those revision levels in their bills of material. They cannot trust their item identification numbers.

Any organization that chooses to include a revision level along with the item identification number within its bills of material is going down the wrong path. Now it has to make more rules about what the revision level means. Now it is forced into controlling procurement and inventory by revision level. Once an organization goes down this path, it is no longer sure of what is, and is not, truly interchangeable.

Bills of material provide an effective way to control applications of most anything, provided they are used properly. They can be used to identify the source code files to be compiled into a software program. Again, the key element is the identification number used to identify each source code file. The degree to which the rules of interchangeability and reidentification are being followed must be considered.

Item Identification Numbers: Length and Format

Identification numbers are preferably short, not long. The characters that make up the number are preferably numeric, not alpha. Any symbols to be used along with the numeric characters are preferably limited to dashes. Revision levels are preferably excluded from the identification number.

These preferences apply to item identification numbers which contain no significance. Preferred formats for significant numbers are described on page 82.

"Short" identification numbers means that it should not be any longer than necessary. If the total population of unique physical item configurations is not expected to exceed 1,000, the length of the basic number does not have to exceed four or five digits. If the total population of unique configurations is expected to go beyond 100,000, then the basic number should be at least six or seven digits.

Figure 8-1 provides an example of a numbering convention commonly used for hardware-oriented products within the defense contract environment as prescribed in MIL-STD-100C, *Engineering Drawing Practices*, 1978. This standard, which is no longer active, included a rule that the drawing number and the item identification number had to be the same or, if not, the drawing number had to be included in the item identification number. It also allowed similar, yet unique, items to be defined on the same drawing. Some of the concepts still have merit.

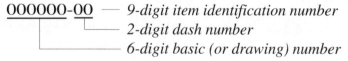

000000-00 — *9-digit item identification number*
                   2-digit dash number
                   6-digit basic (or drawing) number

Figure 8-1   9-digit item identification number that includes a dash number.

Appropriate numbering conventions are influenced by many factors. Ease with which inquiries can be made via the ID number is one. Interchangeability and ability to trust identification numbers is another. The cost required to reidentify items and revise their supporting documentation is a third factor.

Pros and Cons of Significant Numbers

An item identification number is considered to be significant when one or more of its digits have meaning. Significant digits are used to provide insight to an item's physical, functional and/or management attributes. Physical and functional attributes range from type of material to performance ratings. Management attributes range from the company that owns the design to the plant where the item is produced.

Standard part catalogs have been widely used for over 50 years to identify standard items such as fasteners, resistors, capacitors and raw materials. Figure 8-2 provides an example of how significant numbers could be used to identify a like-family of flat washers. This approach allows hundreds of unique washer configurations to be defined with a single drawing. No additional drawing effort is required to activate a new configuration. It is noted that the alpha and numeric characters are purposely alternated to enhance clarity.

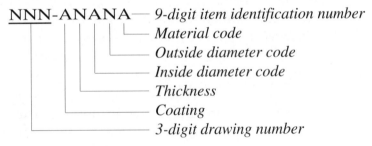

Figure 8-2   9-digit significant number for a like-family of flat washers.

The major advantage of significant numbers, per this example, is the reduced cost of documentation. The drawing number can be relatively short since the population of like-families of standard items is relatively small.

Problems with significance are most likely to occur when inserting management attributes into the codes. Such practice should be avoided. Most information of this nature is readily available through automated tools. The pros and cons of significance must be evaluated in each case accordingly.

Naming Conventions for Physical Items

Naming conventions represent how physical items are named and described. Physical items from families of like-items should carry the same name. For example, bolts are bolts, washers are washers, capacitors are capacitors, and so on. Generic nouns are used to assign names.

Each physical item, once named, is briefly described in terms of its physical and functional attributes. Those attributes are preferably described in their descending order of significance. The appropriate descriptions include four, five or six of the most important attributes. Those descriptions may also be abbreviated. The name and description can be limited to 30 or so digits and still be highly informative.

Such naming conventions provide an effective way to identify the similarities and differences between the total population of physical items which are currently being used. To be effective, there must be a high degree of consistency in how the conventions are applied. It is thereafter simply a matter of sorting on the names and descriptions.

The required consistency is easily achieved by using a computer program to identify the hierarchy of possible attributes for each named item. Such a program also identifies the possible aliases for each named item. If the wrong name should happen to be selected, that will become evident while going through the hierarchy of possible attributes.

Once a name is selected, its aliases should appear along with the choices within the first attribute. If those choices are correct, the name is probably correct. Selection of a first choice should prompt the next set of choices. Such prompts continue until the item is fully described.

An organization that goes through this process for the first time will discover many redundancies. It will find several cases in which the same item exists under two or more identification numbers. Such a naming process makes it possible to identify and eliminate such redundancies and also take advantage of reuse opportunities.

Equivalent and Alternate Item Files

Items under different identification numbers that are fully interchangeable are referred to as *equivalent* items. Such items should be cross-referenced in a file that can be accessed by all activities throughout the organization. Such a file would include the item identification number, its name and the organization that assigned that number and name.

The *equivalent item file* would include any items whose internally-assigned identification numbers are known to be redundant. It would include vendor-supplied items wherein the vendor-assigned identification number coexists with an internally-assigned identification number. It would include items supplied to customers wherein they assign their own identification numbers.

An alternate item, per the CMII methodology, is one that may be temporarily used in place of a preferred item. Such an authorization may be stated in terms of time or quantity. Such temporary usage may also be limited to a specific application. An ECN-type of approval is needed each time an alternate item is to be used in place of a preferred item. It is appropriate to maintain a cross-reference between preferred items, their acceptable alternates, actual usages of the alternates and the associated authorizations.

Alternate items are typically used to compensate for a shortage of the preferred items. As-planned and as-released baselines include only the preferred items. That is not the appropriate place to identify the acceptable alternates. The alternate item file serves that purpose.

As-built records associated with each work authorization should include the actual bill of material used to produce the product. Such bills are revised at the time the work authorization is released if it is known that a preferred item is not available. Although the planning bills show only the preferred item, the as-built records show the item that was actually used. Again, the authorization for using an alternate item is maintained in the alternate item file.

Superseded and Superseding Item History File

Configurations continue to change throughout all phases of their life cycle. Components are superseded by other components. Entire structures or assemblies are superseded by other structures or assemblies. Some item replacements arc one-to-one. Some are many-to-one or one-to-many. Some are many-to-many.

Development and production-oriented activities work with the current and/or the latest configurations. The activities involved in support and maintenance do not have this luxury. They must maintain the entire fleet of in-service units which may represent many different versions of the same model. Such in-service units may not have been identical when they were built and delivered. Every support activity must learn how to work through such differences. The appropriate superseded and superseding item history file can be very beneficial in this regard.

It should be possible to search for any physical item by its internally-assigned identification number and determine if it has been superseded. If it has, and if the replacement is one-to-one, the identification number of the superseding item should appear along with its authorization and effectivity. Any special instructions for using the superseding item, if required, should also appear.

In the cases where the superseded and superseding items are not one-to-one, the change authorization (ECN number) should appear in the field where the superseding number would normally appear. This serves to signify that the ECN must be reviewed to determine the appropriate action. Those who maintain bills of material should also maintain the superseded and superseding item history file.

Such a file is especially valuable to activities that order spare parts to support their in-service equipment. It is also valuable to the activities that receive those orders. Such a file is also useful to those responsible for keeping pending change effectivities properly synchronized.

Model Numbers

A *model number* is an identifier that organizations use to identify their end-item products for sales and marketing purposes. A name is sometimes used in place of a number. Automobile companies, for example, tend to use names. Aircraft manufacturers tend to use numbers. Model numbers, or names, are attractive because they are typically short, simple and easy to remember.

There is no industry standard for how to assign model numbers or names. Some conventions, however, are better than others for supporting the CMII objectives. Figure 8-3 provides an example of the model designation for a Boeing 737.

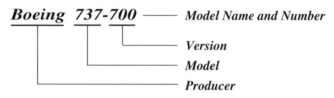

Figure 8-3   Example of a model number.

Most products that have model numbers also have serial numbers. A model number is very similar to what is traditionally known as a "configuration item number." Directions on how to use configuration item numbers were provided in the military standards which are no longer active. They were to be comprised of seven digits. Serial numbers were to be assigned relative to the configuration item number and were to begin with one in each case.

It is noted that the vehicle identification number for most automobiles represents a number with significance followed by a serial number. A company that provides automobile insurance can determine what the rate should be (size of engine, and so on) based on the vehicle identification number.

For CMII purposes, each like-family of end-items should have its own as-planned and as-released baseline. The model number is a good starting point for identifying like-families.

Conventions for Identifying Software

Traditional practices used by software developers to identify source code files and software programs are very different from the practices used by manufacturing companies to identify their products. Figure 8-4 provides an example of how a commercial, off-the-shelf software product is identified. This example is similar to the convention used by manufacturers to assign model numbers.

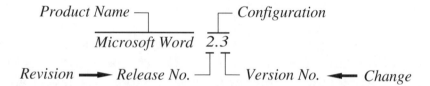

Figure 8-4   Example of convention used to identify commercial software.

Advancement of the release number is called a *revision*. Advancement of the version number is called a *change*.

Figure 8-5 provides an example plus a brief explanation of a convention for identifying source code files.

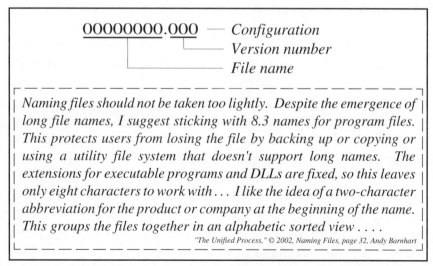

Figure 8-5   Example of convention used to identify source code files.

Chapter 8 — Summary

Ability to manage a variety of configurations depends upon the integrity of the naming and numbering conventions that are being used. Identification numbers are used to control applications and interchangeability. Naming conventions are used to name and describe physical items.

Widely accepted standards for naming or numbering, however, do not exist. Outside of a few articles, no authoritative books have been published. Although naming and numbering conventions are still underdeveloped, they are more mature in manufacturing than in software development communities.

Identification numbers are preferably short, not long. The characters are preferably numeric, not alpha. Symbols, if used, are preferably limited to dashes. Revision levels are preferably excluded from the identification number.

An item identification number is significant when one or more of its characters have meaning. Significant numbers provide a way to reduce the cost of documentation. Management attributes should not be included as significance.

Positive control of physical item applications is achieved through bills of material to the degree that identification numbers can be trusted. Lack of trust is why the revision level of each physical item is often included in the bills of material.

Naming conventions provide the ability to identify similarities and differences between physical items, thereby providing visibility to support their reuse. Consistency in how physical items are named and described is a prerequisite.

Fully interchangeable items with different identification numbers are recognized as *equivalents*. Items temporarily used in place of preferred items are recognized as *alternates*.

It should be possible to determine the superseded and superseding status of any physical item by its identification number. This ability is needed in all product life cycle phases.

Like-families of end-items are identified by a model number which is equivalent to a configuration item number. Each model has its own as-planned and as-released baseline.

9
Data Integrity

Any information that could impact safety, quality, schedule, cost, profit or the environment must be managed.

Organizational performance is a function of the number of data sets used in-series and the integrity level of each set.

Overall performance declines exponentially as the integrity level of data sets used in-series declines.

An organization cannot escape the corrective action mode until the integrity level of each data set approaches 100%.

We are in the computer age when organizations depend completely on data. Data exists in many forms. Although we may try to distinguish between data, documents, forms and records, data is still a catch-all term. It includes all information used to run the business. Information is derived from data. Organizations that run on inaccurate data operate in a corrective action mode. They are trying to run on quicksand.

Data integrity has not yet taken its turn as a quality initiative. Organizations have yet to learn how their performance correlates with various levels of integrity. They do not bother with integrity measurements. They are running blind. If they understood the correlation, they would make high integrity a top priority. This chapter describes the importance of data integrity and how to improve integrity levels.

Dependent Demand and Netted Requirements

Each individual in an organization works to requirements. Requirements are communicated in the form of plans. High-level plans are extended into detailed plans. Detailed plans are communicated in the form of planning bills, process plans and schedules and thereby convey the what, how and when on an item-by-item basis. All three ingredients — what, how and when — represent data.

The project management cycle, as described on page 36, is a closed-loop cycle comprised of four steps; plan, do, study and act. The "plan" step is the most important. It is the basis for the other steps. The plan step enables the "do" step. The plan step is the basis for the "study" step. The plan is updated by the "act" step.

Netted requirements represent the work that remains to be accomplished. Work to be accomplished is derived by subtracting work already accomplished from the amount originally planned. To illustrate the importance of data integrity, suppose the amount of work originally planned was 90% accurate and the work actually accomplished is 90% accurate. Consequently, the plan for work remaining to be accomplished is only 81% (.90 x .90 = .81) accurate.

Dependent demand and *independent demand* are terms commonly used in a master scheduling function wherein the materials and resources needed to achieve the master schedule are defined via a hierarchy of planning bills. The number of indenture levels can range from two to many. It is like a chain. The requirements at each descending level are dependent upon the demands for the parent-level items. An item has independent demands if it is master scheduled. An item has dependent demands if it resides at a level below a master scheduled item. An item can have both types of demands.

All of this becomes important when trying to identify the number of data sets being used in-series. The requirements for each item residing at each level within the hierarchy of planning bills must be netted. The netting process may be repeated on a daily basis. It begins at the top of the hierarchy and proceeds level by level until it reaches the bottom. The netted requirements for an item residing eight levels deep can be very different from one day to the next. The associated resources work in a state of confusion accordingly.

How Data Integrity Influences Performance

Figure 9-1 shows a correlation between employee effectiveness and data integrity. The curve is based on eight data sets used in-series and shows how overall effectiveness declines or improves as data integrity declines or improves. The relationship is exponential.

R is the resources required to do the work when all data sets are 100% accurate. Resources must be added as the level of integrity declines. If using eight data sets in-series, and the average level of integrity declines from 100% to 92%, twice as many resources are needed to do the same work. Fortunately, the reverse is also true.

This empirical formula correlates very closely to practical experience. The key point is this: The goal for integrity must be 100%. Anything below 100% is not acceptable. Plans for achieving and maintaining a high level of integrity deserve top priority.

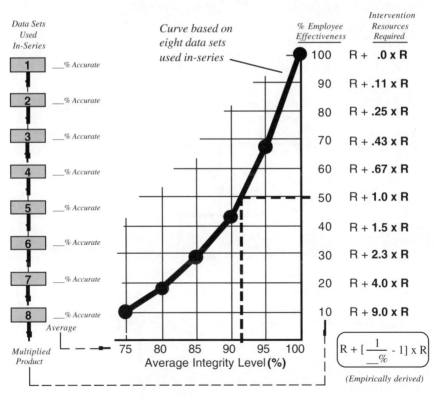

Figure 9-1   Organizational performance as a function of data integrity.

Example of Data Sets Used In-Series

Computerized processes are often referred to as "job streams." Once such a process is initiated, the computer goes through a series of commands and extracts information from specific databases. The extracted information is carried forth and summarized. The information derived from one job stream may be the input to another. The integrity of the end result is proportional to the (1) number of job streams, (2) number of databases in each job stream, and (3) level of integrity of each database.

Enterprise requirements planning, or ERP, systems use many databases in-series. Such automated systems start at the top of a physical item hierarchy, as shown in Figure 9-2, and work downward level by level to calculate planned receipts and issues for each item at each level in each time period. Scheduled receipts and issues for the lowest-level buy items are highly prone to error.

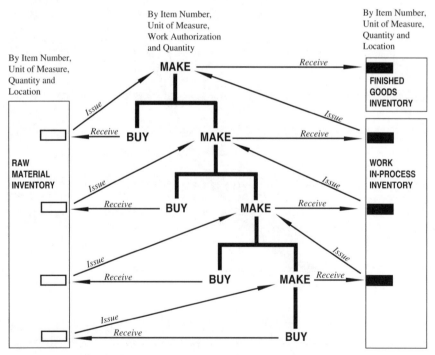

Figure 9-2   Planning bills for scheduling physical item receipts and issues.

Inaccurate Data: Root Causes Are Interdependent

The legal expression, "no harm, no foul," is appropriate for this discussion. The objective is to measure the amount of harm that results when the "foul" is inaccurate data. Three factors must be considered. One is how to know when data is, in fact, inaccurate. Another is how to quantify the impact. The third is how to identify and segregate other possible causes.

First, the organization must be requirements-driven and there must be positive control of all work. All work must be initiated by the appropriate forms and accomplished in a closed-loop process. Authorizing forms and specified requirements must remain in the loop until the results conform. These are best practices that every organization should follow.

A work authorization is written for one of two reasons, first-time work or rework. To rework is to redo something that was not done right the first time. Time spent on a job is recorded against the work authorization. Time spent doing jobs right and time spent redoing jobs are derived from the time records. Such time-charging can be accomplished on a sampling basis and with minimum effort.

If the initial results associated with authorized work do not conform, they are reworked until they do. Why the rework was necessary becomes the big question. Was it lack of proper skills? Lack of proper training? A deficient process? Deficient requirements? Inaccurate data?

Once the requirements and the processes used to achieve those requirements are both validated by actual users, it is easy to sift out the real root causes for nonconformances. This is also a best practice that every organization should follow. Those that involve users in such a manner make a profound discovery — data integrity improves and nonconformances go away.

Root causes for nonconformances are so intertwined that they cannot be segregated into distinct categories. Nonconformances and all root causes disappear when requirements are assured of being clear, concise and valid for each user. Requirements include what is to be done and how it is to be done. Assuring data integrity is part of the process.

Data Integrity Must Be a Quality Initiative

Organizations continue to spend an ever-increasing amount of money each year to automate their business processes. The purpose of such automation is to improve their competitiveness. Unless there is a concurrent effort to improve the integrity of requirements (including data), the expected benefits of automation will not be forthcoming.

The resources that organizations spend on intervention are estimated in various trade magazines to range from 20 to 40%. Those estimates are grossly understated. Statistics compiled by the Institute of Configuration Management indicate that over half of today's organizations are spending 40 to 60% of their resources on intervention. Any organization that is spending close to 40% of its resources on intervention should not make automation its top priority.

Furthermore, a review of the most popular tools being used in those automation efforts reveal that the functionality needed to accommodate change and assure that requirements remain clear, concise and valid does not represent the strength of those tools. In fact, overall functionality is not even viewed from that perspective. It is clearly obvious that the process must be fixed first. The process must lead and the enabling tools must follow.

Organizations implementing such enabling tools must learn that migrating data from legacy systems to the new system does not mean that data integrity is being improved. Data migration must not be confused with improving data integrity. They are separate issues. Any interdependencies are relatively minor.

Any organization that is spending over 20% of its resources on intervention needs to make data integrity its top priority. Until it understands the process improvements that are needed to improve data integrity, only then will it know what the enabling tools need to do. Attempts to specify the required functionality prior to that understanding will do nothing but specify the wrong requirements.

The point is this: Data integrity must become a quality initiative. Of all business process improvement initiatives that continue to come along, data integrity has not been one of them. "Zero defects" was on the right track but that initiative focused on the product. To hit the bull's-eye, the focus must be on data integrity.

Harnessing the Power of Creators and Users

Empowerment of employees was, without doubt, the most positive benefit derived from the Total Quality Management movement. It was a major paradigm shift to accept the belief that workers have brains. There was also a negative side. There were some who concluded that empowered employees do not need leadership. Some stopped updating their organizational charts. Some turned them upside down. Some tossed them away completely.

The best way to empower employees is to make them creators and users. Every employee, from the top to the very bottom of an organization, uses documentation and data. The hierarchy of administrative documents used to run the business, and their assigned owners, should emulate the organizational hierarchy. The physical item hierarchies and supporting documents for each item at each level within those hierarchies, as well as their assigned owners, should emulate the skill levels of the design and process specialists and the touch labor that builds those physical items.

Each and every document must be co-owned by an assigned creator and one or more designated users. The lowest-level workers cannot be excluded. The individual that has to use a document and achieve the intended results is the one who knows best if that document is clear, concise and valid.

There is no better way to create an environment in which employees can take pride in their work. Every employee is a creator and/or a user. The user of a higher-level document is the creator of a subordinate-level document. The output from one individual represents the input to another individual. It is an excellent way to get employees motivated and keep them motivated. Such assignments, however, must be done properly.

Assignments, once made, must remain relatively stable. Workloads must be fairly balanced. Each individual must be given a fair chance to make their assigned documents free of difficulty. The effort that co-owners must take to upgrade their assigned documents must be minimized. Co-owners who are best at making their assigned documents free of difficulty must be recognized and rewarded. Good management is essential.

Requirements Do Not Have to Be Perfect

Latent fear of the word "requirements" must be overcome. That fear must be replaced with unwavering confidence that clear, concise and valid requirements are not only possible, but also essential. A similar fear of data and the law of diminishing returns must also be replaced with unwavering confidence that a goal of 100% accuracy is possible and also essential.

Such confidence does not mean that requirements have to be perfect. Requirements represent plans that are like forecasts. All organizations work to forecasts. It is often said that forecasts are always wrong. It is true that they are rarely correct in all details in the distant future. That is OK. They do not need to be perfect in all details. They need to be correct in the things that matter in that time period. They will be refined as they move closer. They need to remain accurate in the things that matter in each time period.

It is appropriate to go back to the analogy of a tree that was provided in chapter 6. The tree trunk and its major branches need to be defined before the details of the smaller limbs and leaves can be defined. The requirements are therefore ever evolving, which means that they are in a continual state of change. That should be viewed as a positive, rather than a negative, situation.

All the wrong things happen when the change process is excessively slow and cumbersome. Administrative procedures, for example, are written before the requirements that the procedure is to achieve have been defined, documented, validated and released. Source code, as another example, is often written before the requirements that the code is to achieve have been defined, documented, validated and released.

Such wrong practices must be, and can be, eliminated. The excuse that it is impossible to write good requirements is simply wrong. The major obstacles can be boiled down to how changes are accommodated and how requirements are assured of being clear, concise and valid.

Regulated Versus Non-Regulated Industries

It is often said that you need configuration management only if you work in a regulated industry. Industries often cited as examples include those which produce military equipment, commercial aircraft or medical devices and those which operate commercial nuclear power plants. The regulating government agencies, in those cases, include the U.S. Department of Defense, Federal Aviation Administration, Food and Drug Administration, the Nuclear Regulatory Commission, and so on.

The requirements contained in the regulations are very similar in each case. Product designs must be defined and documented. Processes used to produce those products must be defined and documented. Changes to those designs and processes must be controlled. The documents in both cases must be controlled. Personnel must be trained. Records of work actually accomplished must be maintained. The records must provide evidence that designs and processes were approved, that processes were followed, and that as-delivered products did conform to approved requirements.

ISO 9000 imposes similar requirements but they are not called configuration management. Companies that are regulated are audited periodically. Companies that are ISO-certified are assessed periodically. Auditors and assessors visit your site and verify that you are doing what you are supposed to do.

No organization is immune to safety, quality, schedule, cost, profit or environmental issues or legal liabilities. What do regulated and nonregulated companies do differently? What would a company do differently if an auditor or assessor was, or was not, looking over its shoulder? How much more does it cost to do business when someone periodically checks to see if you are doing what you are supposed to do? What corners would you cut if there was no auditor? How much would you save?

An organization that is afraid of an auditor lacks confidence in its processes. Every organization should want to have a showcase process that can be paraded in front of customers and regulators at every opportunity. From a CM point of view, that showcase process is the same whether the organization is regulated or not.

Chapter 9 — Summary

Data integrity, in itself, has little meaning. It is the impact of inaccurate data that has meaning. The correlation between level of data integrity and overall performance must be understood. Only then is it possible to understand the current state and where the priorities need to be placed.

We are in the computer age when organizations run on data. Data exists in many forms. Information is derived from data. Organizations that run on inaccurate data operate in a corrective action mode. It is like trying to run on quicksand.

Data integrity has yet to take its turn as a quality initiative. Organizations have not learned how performance correlates with levels of integrity. They do not measure the impact of poor data. They are running blind. Once they know the correlation, data integrity will become a high priority.

An appreciation for data integrity is gained by reviewing what happens when data sets are used in-series. The potential problem grows as the number of data sets used in-series increases. It is the in-series aspect that causes intervention resources to grow exponentially as the average level of integrity of each data set declines.

Whatever eliminates problems with safety, quality, schedule, cost or profit will also eliminate problems in the other categories. Nonconformances and their root causes disappear when requirements are assured of being clear, concise and valid for each user. This includes assuring that data is accurate. Data integrity must be established as a quality initiative.

All organizations need a process that can accommodate change and maintain integrity in all associated data. It is not something that regulated industries need more than nonregulated industries. All organizations need to do the same things whether or not a third party is looking over their shoulder.

Each document must be co-owned by a creator and one or more users. The lowest-level workers cannot be excluded. The person that must use a document and achieve its specified results knows best if it is what it should be. Each document and/or data set must be free of difficulty for each user.

10

The "V" Model for Development

*Development is a three-phase, eight-step process wherein
configurations are designed top-down and produced bottom-up.*

*The first two steps of development serve to define the end-item
application requirements and the basis for detailed design.*

*The success of any development effort will be proportional to the
reliability and efficiency of the CM process.*

*Legally, a failure in CM is a failure to use due care.
A product that is not as-promised is due to a failure in CM.*

Any development process that is not requirements-driven
has a high probability of failure. It is impossible to be requirements-
driven and not have an effective configuration management process.
It does not matter whether development projects are large or small.
The larger they are, the harder they fall when these prerequisites are
missing.

Configuration management is not something to be imposed
after development is completed. It must be an integral part of
development. It is an essential ingredient that enables development
to be successful.

This chapter describes a three-phase, eight-step process that
is appropriate for any development effort. It is a requirements-driven
process. It works best when enabled by a configuration management
process that is reliable and efficient.

Development: Three Phases with Eight Steps

The development process, per the CMII model, is comprised of eight steps, as displayed in Table 10-1.

High-level plan	1	*Define end-item application requirements*
	2	*Develop basis for detailed design*
Detailed plan	3	*a. Define physical item hierarchy or architecture*
		b. Identify primary documents and their owners
	4	*Identify secondary items and documents*
	5	*Define document release schedules*
Execute plan	6	*Create, validate and release required documents*
	7	*Build the product and verify conformance*
	8	*Resolve any nonconformances as needed*

Table 10-1   Development process.

Steps 1 and 2 create the high-level plan. The high-level plan includes the application requirements for the product to be developed along with a high-level definition of that product. The application requirements represent what the product *must do*. The high-level definition of the product provides the basis for detailed design and represents what the product *can do*.

Steps 3, 4 and 5 expand the high-level plan into a detailed plan. Step 3 serves to define the overall physical item hierarchy or architecture and the primary documents. Step 4 serves to define the secondary items and documents. Step 5 serves to define the release schedule for each primary and secondary document.

Steps 6, 7 and 8 execute the detailed plan. Step 6 creates, validates and releases the required documents. The validation step includes any prototyping that may be needed. The product is built and conformance is verified in step 7. Any nonconformances detected during step 7 are resolved in step 8.

Steps 7 and 8 will be relatively uneventful if the planning steps, 1 through 6, are properly carried out. Resources needed to complete steps 7 and 8 could easily double or triple if planning steps are skipped or not brought to proper closure.

Design Basis Documents: Four Types

The application requirements must not be confused with the basis for detailed design. The application requirements represent what the product *must do* in its operational state. The design basis represents what the product *can do*. The *must do's* must be segregated from the *can do's*.

The design basis documents to be created in step 2 of the development process provide a high-level definition of what the end-item product is to be, how it will be produced and how it will be supported. Four types of documents are usually adequate for defining the design basis for most products, regardless of their complexity.

Those documents typically include (a) one or more functional specifications which describe what the product can do, (b) system architecture or schematics which describe how the product does what it can do, (c) layouts and perhaps interface drawings which describe overall appearance and the relationships between physical items, and (d) one or more process plans for how to produce, operate and maintain the product.

Each document type can be, and should be, relatively brief. This is where major trade-offs between the customer's needs and internal capabilities, if any, are resolved. This is the proper place to verify that the as-planned product can support the application requirements. However, this is not the time to get into excessive detail; the design details can come later.

Once the high-level plan is validated and released, the development effort may proceed to the next step. The detailed planning effort, although very involved and time intensive, should be relatively straightforward. The execution phase should go smoothly if all planning steps are properly completed. Any deficiencies will come to light in step 7. The intervention resources required to resolve those deficiencies are spent in step 8.

The importance of the high-level plan, and the detailed plans which follow, cannot be overly emphasized. A development effort that starts out on the right foot has a higher probability of success than one which does not. An effective CM process is essential for getting the right start and keeping the effort on-track.

Design Basis Extended into Detailed Designs

Step 3 of the eight-step development process focuses on product structure. This is where the end-item configuration, whatever it may be, is subdivided into its hierarchy of modules, components and/or raw materials. This very important step must be accomplished by the appropriate cross-functional team. Those who created the design basis in step 2 should participate in step 3.

Each document required to support each physical item within the hierarchy or architecture is identified in step 3. This includes all design and process-related documents. During this step, the team members representing each of the downstream activities make sure their needs are addressed. Creators and designated users for each primary document are also assigned.

Step 4 is best accomplished by the creator and designated user team that co-owns the primary process document containing secondary items and documents. The creators for such process documents are typically process engineers while the users of those are typically those who perform the work on physical items.

Step 5 is a scheduling step and should be achieved by the same cross-functional team that completed step 3. The appropriate project management tools are beneficial for performing this scheduling task. The detailed development plan is accomplished with the completion of steps 3, 4 and 5.

At that point, it becomes possible to drive all development resources with one set of priorities. Although there may be exceptions, the greatest percentage of the development resources are spent in step 6 where documents are created, validated and released. The resources spent in step 6 should be greater than those spent in step 7. Products built in step 7 will be "right the first time" to the degree that the detailed requirements are clear, concise and valid.

As previously stated on page 11, the primary product of development is documentation and the purpose of a prototype is to proof the documentation. The effort required to complete development steps 7 and 8 increases exponentially as the integrity of the documentation declines. Again, if planning steps 1 through 6 were perfect, there would be no surprises in steps 7 and 8.

Planned Versus Evolutionary Development

Table 10-2 contrasts the advantages of a planned design approach to development, as discussed on the previous pages, with an evolutionary approach. Evolutionary design is most commonly used in software development.

IS DESIGN DEAD?

Two styles of design are used in software development: evolutionary and planned design. Perhaps the most common is evolutionary design. Essentially, it means a system's design grows as the system is implemented. Design is part of the programming process. As the program evolves, the design changes.

In its common usage, evolutionary design is a disaster. The design ends up being the aggregation of ad hoc tactical decisions, each of which makes the code harder to alter. Not only does this make the software harder to change, it also makes bugs easier to breed and harder to find and safely kill. This is the "code and fix" nightmare where the bugs become exponentially more expensive to fix as the project goes on.

Planned design is counter to this. Designers think through big issues in advance. They work at a more abstract level. Once the design is done, they hand it off to someone else to build.

The planned design approach has been around since the '70s. It's better in many ways than code-and-fix evolutionary design, but it has some faults. First, it is impossible to think through all of the issues you need to deal with when you are programming. When programmers find things that question the design, they start coding around it — and entropy sets in. It takes time to sort out the problems and alter the code accordingly.

The second fault, and the biggest of headaches, is changing requirements. One way to deal with it is to build flexibility into the design. However, this requires insight into what kind of changes you expect. You have to understand the requirements well enough to separate the volatile areas, and this is very hard.

"Is Design Dead?" Martin Fowler, www.martinfowler.com/articles/designDead.html

---

Table 10-2   Planned versus evolutionary approach to development.

Too Little CM Versus Too Much CM

It is generally accepted that small development projects involving relatively few individuals do not require as much formality as big projects with numerous participants. It is also generally accepted that people with higher skill levels do not require as much formality as those with lower skill levels.

"Formality" is the key word. Formality pertains to the documented rules and/or procedures that must be followed while performing the development tasks. It includes the oversight required to ensure that the rules and procedures are being followed. Such formality becomes most significant in the area of configuration management because that is where the most controversial rules reside.

A discussion of too much or too little formality in the development process is overly vague. The real issue is whether or not configuration management is needed by asking pertinent questions. Should the process used in development be more lenient than the process used during production or should the same requirements apply? Does configuration management prevent development from being fast and efficient? Is configuration management something that should be practiced after the product leaves development?

Nor is it a matter of too much or too little process but rather of process reliability and efficiency. Any process that is reliable and efficient will be used and appreciated by its users. Conversely, any process perceived as slow and cumbersome will be criticized. It is safe to conclude that users who cannot see forthcoming improvements will likely look for ways to work around that process.

The question boils down to how much configuration management is enough. What is the boundary between too much and too little? Does the boundary differ from project to project? Are there rules or principles that are good for some projects and not others? From a CMII perspective, such differences do not exist.

According to the CMII model, the rules and principles should be the same for every project during both development and production. Such a paradigm shift will not be achieved until the CM process is truly reliable and efficient. Even so, the evidence will clearly establish that a poor CM process is better than no process.

Rescue of Software Documentation and Code

Table 10-3 documents steps to take when dealing with common software development practices and needed improvements. This insight was gleaned by the author from his extensive experience in rescuing troubled software projects.

STEP ONE: DETERMINE THE PROJECT REQUIREMENTS
  You know when a project is in trouble right away: it usually has the worst in project management, code quality and customer expectations. You have to figure out the requirements and make sense of the source code before you can begin to tackle the problems.

  Before you can fix the project, you must know what you're supposed to accomplish. This has three overlapping components: the requirements document, the minimal set of features needed, and short- and long-term issues.

  You'll probably have some kind of requirements document. It may even be accurate. If the project were well-managed enough to have proper requirements tracking, it wouldn't be a disaster. Most likely, you'll have to rummage through a pile of binders and folders to find contract documents, meeting and phone notes, and so on.

  One of the first things you'll want to do is find the programmers who worked on the project. No, not for programming instruction! The previous programmers generally have an idea of what the project was supposed to do. Although they may be hazy on details, they might be willing to give you the nickel tour and flesh out any notes they left.

  Projects for outside customers are likely to have a paper trail. This may not be a clear trail, what with written amendments, undocumented promises, and the like; however, it's a start. "Inside" jobs are more likely to be specified informally at best. The best procedure is to sort everything by date where possible, write up what you can, and have it reviewed. Expect changes, even if you did a perfect job of reconstruction, because management requirements will have evolved.

  While you are deducing the requirements document, divide the requirements into several categories, including "essential for first version," "can wait for a later version," and "nonessential." The category of any feature doesn't matter much, but it is important to prioritize the features. You will be hard-pressed to get anything done in time, and you can't be burdened with nonessentials.

Table 3 (continued)   Balance short- and long-term goals. You should want to build a masterpiece, but if the project is two delays from the chopping block, the final straw may be your effort on some long-term issue that doesn't get the product out the door next month.

Decide on the quality that must be present in the final product. Attention to quality usually results in reduced time and cost for new projects. Be prepared for a tough fight with management on this. The idea of "ship it now, fix it later" is so obvious that every manager reinvents it. Studies, statistics and logic don't persuade them, so either give in on the issue or insert quality on the sly.

STEP TWO: FIGURE OUT THE SOURCE CODE

Most programmers see source code as the heart of the project. I don't quite agree. The requirements document and project management procedures have at least as much to do with eventual success or failure. But I can see their point: if the source code doesn't make a working project, you've got nothing. Examining the source code is a universal step since every project will have it, but many don't have a requirements document, standards, or other frippery. The source code is, of course, its own document. (Yes, that's a joke).

But it's not as much of a joke as it should be. Unfortunately, you cannot rely on any documentation you might find. Requirements and design documents are notoriously out-of-date; programmer's notebooks are often illegible and incomplete; and source comments are typically outdated, useless, or just plain wrong. Odds are, the previous team made several variations of the project in different directories, and didn't document any of the locations or the reasons for making them. Also, version control probably isn't being used properly, if at all.

You'll usually have to go over the source code, line by line, to figure out what it's doing. That's not necessarily what it should be doing, but it's the baseline where you'll start in making the project work.

Generally, the source code will not be of a quality that anyone would care to brag about. A big problem is inconsistency: in indentation, variable names, and everything else. It's not usually worth the time and effort to stop all work and bring all the code up to standard. Instead, it's OK to fix each module when you need to work on it for other reasons.

Break down large functions. Most projects in trouble seem to have a number of very large routines. This is probably because the programmers had sloppy habits and were also under the gun to add just one more feature or to patch an error, and thought that sloppy code could

Table 3 (continued)   always be fixed later. In any event, code tends to accrete, comments get out-of-date, and any hypothetical clarity of design morphs into obscurity.

You'll want to break these large functions into smaller chunks, mainly for comprehension now but also for maintainability. One way is to lift large, relatively autonomous pieces and turn them into routines. Really messed-up code won't have any chunks that you can extract and call without a dozen or so arguments.

Another method of making sense of undocumented legacy code is literate programming, invented by Donald Knuth. Literate programming is the combination of source code and documentation in the same source file, with emphasis on clear exposition for the human reader. Your goal as a literate programmer is to describe the program in a technical article, which, incidentally, can be processed by a tool to create the program's source code.

A literate source file consists of blocks of descriptive text interleaved with blocks of code most often called "chunks." Chunks may contain references to other chunks as well as target language code, and may in turn, be contained in higher-level chunks. The program that makes the program code from your literate program is essentially a macro expander that starts from a root chunk and expands all references to other chunks until it ends up with straight source code.

A key point of literate programming is that the code chunks should be small enough that a reader can easily grasp the function of each chunk. You don't need to write chunks in the order in which the compiler needs to see them. Instead, present them in whatever order makes the program clearest to the reader. You can detail the interwoven discussion as you like, using mathematical equations, tables, diagrams, or anything else you need to get the point across.

My usual technique, in the analysis of legacy code, is to make each routine into a single chunk, then work my way through the large chunk, extracting loops, conditionals, conceptual blocks, and the like into nested chunks. By the time I'm done, I'll have turned an 800-line function into a few dozen chunks of abut 20 statements each, and most chunks will have a description of a few lines to a couple of pages. These are much easier to grasp than the original behemoth.

After you've cleaned up the source code, you can proceed through the development process, which should run just like any other project.   "Saving a Project in Trouble" by Steve Furlong, p 129-133, The Unified Process, © 2002

Table 10-3   Steps to rescue a troubled software development project.

Rescue Steps Relative to CMII

Several of Steve Furlong's recommendations (see Table 10-3) on how to save a troubled software development project are consistent with the CMII principles. He recommends large and complex modules be broken down into more manageable increments and that each increment be defined and documented in a manner that is most clear to other users.

The CMII approach requires that each physical item within the overall hierarchy or architecture have its own unique set of design and process-related documentation. Those documents are written for and validated by the user. That hierarchy is defined by a cross-functional team at an early step in the process and represents the most manageable increments. They also accommodate reuse.

Such a rescue demands working top-down and bottom-up simultaneously. It is necessary to work top-down to figure out what the code should be relative to what it is. It is necessary to work bottom-up to discover what the requirements were meant to be relative to those which could be found.

The CMII approach works top-down and strives not to cycle backward more than one step. A next step is not taken until a prior step is brought to proper closure. As-planned and as-released baselines ratchet forward with each step. Authorization is required for each step and a record is retained with evidence of proper completion.

Furlong also emphasizes the importance of "proper requirements tracking" and "version control." Combined, they provide a good trail of what the initial requirements were and how the documentation and code have evolved since inception. Under the CMII approach, a development effort would not be initiated until these basic elements of configuration management are firmly in place.

Projects as troubled as the one described are never fully rescued. To save the documentation and code is to make it "suitable-for-use." That is the best a rescuer can hope to achieve.

As this illustration makes clear, the activities of development are enabled by the configuration management process. A development effort will be successful to the degree that the configuration management process is reliable and efficient.

Legal View of CM and a Producer's Liabilities

Configuration is what a product is physically and functionally expected to be. Configuration management is a process for controlling products. Configuration management serves to ensure that released documentation controls the physical and functional configuration of products.

A product is anything that results from a person's effort. From a legal point of view, a person is any human, corporation, partnership, government or other legal entity. There is a legal interest when the results of a person's efforts may adversely affect others.

Released documentation is not only a means of controlling the configuration of products, it is also a product itself. Documentation is a means of communicating the required configuration of a product and its associated processes.

Configuration management, under whatever name, is the only way a producer can rationally assure that products conform to explicit and/or implied characteristics. A product that is not as expressly or implicitly promised is due to a failure in configuration management. There is legal liability if the differences cause harm or damage. Such a failure in configuration management is a "breach of contract."

Legally, a producer owes the public at large a product that is safe. To persons with whom the producer contracts, the liability is to assure that the product is as-promised. Configuration management is essential to producing products that conform at all levels.

Torts are civil wrongs which are the basis for law suits. They are not based on contracts. Torts fall into three categories: intentional, negligence and strict liability. Negligent torts happen when a producer did not use due care. A failure in configuration management is a failure to use due care.

The law considers failures in workmanship and material to be "manufacturing defects." It further considers design defects to be a failure to plan properly. Even if the design and workmanship are flawless, marketing defect and failure-to-warn liabilities are still possible. Labels, manuals and instructions must be clear, concise and valid. Such information sets need to be managed and controlled like any other released document.

Chapter 10 — Summary

Any development process that is not requirements-driven has a high probability of failure. It is impossible to be requirements-driven and not have an effective configuration management process regardless of the size of the development project. The larger they are, the harder they fall when configuration management is missing.

The appropriate development process is comprised of three phases and eight steps. The two steps in the first phase serve to prepare a high-level plan by defining the end-item application requirements (what it must do) and the basis for detailed design (what it can do).

The next three steps extend the high-level plan into detailed plans. The three steps of the final phase execute the detailed plans. Any nonconformances to be resolved in step 8 are minimized if planning steps 1 through 6 are carried out properly and the product is build right the first time in step 7.

A development effort that starts out on the right foot has a higher probability of success than one which does not. An effective configuration management process is essential for getting the right start and keeping the effort on-track.

The question boils down to how much configuration management is needed. What is too much or too little? Does the boundary differ from project to project or from development to production? Under CMII, the process is the same across all environments. Regardless of the environment, the process must be reliable and efficient. Until such a process is achieved, however, a poor process is better than none at all.

From a legal point of view, a product that is not as expressly or implicitly promised is due to a failure in configuration management. There is a legal liability if the differences cause harm or damage. Such a failure in configuration management is a "breach of contract."

Under tort laws, negligent torts can occur when producers fail to use due care. A failure in configuration management is a failure to use due care.

11
Work Centers and Process Standards

*Work is planned and accomplished through a network of
internal work centers and external suppliers.*

*Process maturity is derived from the quality of an organization's
design and build standards and how they are used.*

*The network of work centers and suppliers must perform
as a team. The output of one is the input for another.*

*Reliability and utilization are optimized through proper
planning, scheduling, input control and output control.*

The magic of success, in the case of a football team, boils
down to how plays are designed and executed. Crisp blocking
and tackling are standards in which football players must
become proficient. Similarly, the magic to success in the case
of a business enterprise, is in how work is planned and executed. It is in how each job is assured of being done right the
first time. It is in how work loads are kept balanced with
capacity and how priorities are maintained as situations change.

The activities of development are like a job shop environment in that work is accomplished through a network of
work centers. Work flows through the network in the form of
inputs and outputs. The output of one is input to another. Inputs
must be validated and outputs must be verified. Capacity must
be planned and priorities must be controlled.

Work Center Networks and Goals

Work center is a term most commonly used in a manufacturing job shop environment where a variety of similar products are produced in relatively small quantities. Various combinations of the same work centers are used to produce those products as quantities are typically too small to dedicate the entire capacity to a single product. The quantity (or lot size) of each job may range from one to many. Setup time becomes important as a work center completes one job and prepares to start another.

A high-volume production line, by contrast, represents a specific set of work centers aligned and fully dedicated to producing the same item. Setup time is not an issue. Consistent conformance is achieved by ensuring each step in the process is repetitive. The task of scheduling is a matter of specifying the build rate.

Scheduling a matrix of work centers within a job shop environment is many times more complex. End-item build completion schedules must be extended into work schedules for each work center. Production schedulers strive to maintain a steady work load at each work center, minimize backlogs and keep queued jobs properly sequenced. The complexity can be overwhelming when the various factors used to derive the schedule are continually changing.

The ideal state is to achieve the variety of a job shop along with the reliability, volume and efficiency of a dedicated production line. Build-to-order products represent one approach for achieving this state. Products such as automobiles are built with customer-selected options, which are added at each station as vehicles move down the production line. Each finished vehicle becomes a unique configuration per the options selected yet this impressive variety is achieved with minimal compromise to volume, quality and/or efficiency.

These scheduling techniques were developed by industrial engineers and production control specialists over 30 years ago. Although their application generally remains confined to manufacturing, the same techniques are valuable for any activity where various types of work are accomplished by various combinations of the same work centers. In fact, most activities within a business enterprise or a government agency represent a network of work centers.

Change Process: a Classic Work Center Network

No activity is more representative of a job shop environment, or work center network, than the "engineering change" process. No two changes are alike, yet they all flow through various combinations of the same work centers. The tasks required to process each change are repetitive in nature. Typical tasks include assigning control numbers, identifying impacted items and documents, performing technical reviews, estimating costs, making business decisions, planning implementation, updating baselines, revising, validating and releasing documents, retaining records and, so on.

Most engineering change processes are plagued with the same problems commonly found in a job shop environment. One work center can be overloaded with work while another has very little to do. Jobs that have the highest priority move through the entire network rather quickly while others are at a standstill. Discrepancies or defects in the product are often detected downstream rather than in the work center where they were created. Intervention resources spend an enormous amount of time on expediting and corrective action.

The process of planning and implementing approved changes is the most difficult phase of the overall change process. The number of work centers involved in the analysis phase, compared to the planning and implementation phase, is relatively small.

The implementation planning for one approved change includes identification of the required tasks and associated skills, the interdependencies between those tasks and the sequence in which those tasks must be accomplished. It is not difficult to assign a schedule to each task, derive an overall completion date and equate that completion date to an effectivity. This is only the planning step.

The number of work centers required to execute a detailed implementation plan can be extensive. The required work centers, and the resources therein, may still be busy implementing previous changes. A new change may have a higher priority than changes already in work. There may be problems with the changes already in work. And that, a configuration management professional once said, can be like "trying to change a tire on a bicycle while riding the bicycle."

Design and Build Standards

It is appropriate to look inside a work center and identify the ingredients needed to make it reliable and efficient. If the job of a work center is to create and revise a specific type of document, there should be standards on how to perform those tasks. If the skills and techniques for creating a document differ from those necessary for revising the same document, then it may be appropriate to split that work center into two work centers.

Design and build standards may exist in many forms and formats. As already discussed in previous chapters, standardized requirements should be in place for the format of each document of each type and the format of each change form of each type, as well as naming and numbering conventions. These steps are essential for optimizing overall efficiency regardless of the type of industry or environment.

Organizations having problems developing software, as discussed on page 25, should take a close look at their standards for designing software and building source code. A work center that excels in creating the product design is not likely to be skilled at writing code. A work center that excels in writing code in one language may not be equally adept at writing code in another language.

Work center design is all about trust and reliability. To schedule a job into a work center is to trust that the job will be done right. Each work center must do everything within its power to ensure that jobs are done right. Work centers must be subdivided into appropriate "pockets of excellence." The goal is to build trust that assigned tasks will be accomplished correctly in every case. Reliable standards plus the appropriate skills for applying those standards are key ingredients.

Establishing the appropriate network of work centers is a major step, but not the only step. The tasks performed by the various work centers must be kept synchronized and workloads must be kept balanced relative to capacities. Outputs must be verified and inputs must be validated in each case. And above all, defects must be prevented and not passed on.

Identify and Schedule Work Center Tasks

Planning and execution are highly interdependent activities. Good plans properly utilize each work center. Tasks to be accomplished must fit the skills of the work center assigned to do the work.

Development projects, as with any type of project, must be broken down into a specific set of appropriate tasks. This becomes relatively easy when the project planner is able to choose from a shopping list of standardized tasks provided by the work centers and outside suppliers that perform the work. The project planner's effort is reduced to building the appropriate plan from the list of reliable standards.

Project plans are typically provided in the form of a "critical path network." The first cut of a project plan identifies the required tasks and the sequence in which they need to be completed. Specific schedules for each task will depend on the availability of capacity, when needed, at each key work center. Automated scheduling tools can prove very beneficial for this complicated process.

Jobs without a particularly high priority should not be put into work until the resources are available to keep them moving. Once a job does start, delays are to be avoided — nothing good happens to jobs sitting in queue behind other jobs. They simply clog up the work centers and cause confusion. Capacity planning is therefore an essential component of scheduling.

The work centers and skills needed in the analysis phase differ from those needed in the implementation phase. The responsibilities for administration are separated accordingly which helps to ensure that the work centers in each phase are properly managed. Investors also have an interest in how work is done as noted in Table 11-1.

Advice to Investors

"Look for companies that have a vision but are also focused on execution, because without the execution the end of the story can be rather unpleasant for investors."

F. Duane Ackerman, CEO, BellSouth, Streetsmart, Dec, 2001

Table 11-1   A good vision plus ability to plan and execute.

Input Validation and Output Verification

A work center must never knowingly produce defects; if a defect does occur, it must not be passed on to a downstream work center. In most cases, the cost of correction increases exponentially as a defect moves farther and farther downstream before it is detected.

Each work center must have reliable methods for verifying that performed tasks were accomplished correctly. Techniques used to verify conformance must be considered when developing a shopping list of standardized tasks. The standards for performing a task, as well as the standards used to verify that the results conform, must reside in the same work center.

Each work center must not only verify its outputs, it must also validate it has the correct inputs before proceeding to perform assigned work. Such validations represent a double-check on things that upstream work centers have already verified. Because inputs may be coming from more than one upstream work center, it is vital they be validated in terms of individual correctness and also their compatibility.

The forms used to authorize work are an important ingredient for guiding and controlling work flows. Change forms serve a purpose similar to the routings used to guide jobs through various work centers in a manufacturing job shop environment. As discussed in chapter 7, change forms are used as templates to guide work through the various work centers that make up the change process.

As the form moves through each successive work center, information fields are filled in and attachments are referenced as needed (per the standards). The added information represents both the output of one work center and an input to the next.

Again, each output is verified and each input is validated. Any defects are resolved promptly and are not passed on. Completed forms, with their attachments and referenced documents, are retained as a record of what was accomplished. Those records include evidence that the actual results did, in fact, conform to the requirements.

Time Standards and Consolidation of Work

The core business process owners should be responsible for monitoring workloads and ensuring that each work center they oversee has adequate capacity. They should also look for opportunities to increase the amount of work that can be accomplished with existing capacity.

The capacity of each work center must be identified in the terms that best represent its capability. It could be quantity or something else — if, for example, the optimum unit of measure is hours, then workloads must be stated in hours.

The shopping list of standardized tasks performed by the various work centers provides the ideal basis for defining workloads. Each task should be assigned a time standard. It should then be possible to sort through all tasks scheduled to go through each work center in each time period and determine the total workload on a period-by-period basis. Schedules may then be adjusted as needed to balance workloads with capacity.

By consolidating jobs, core business process owners can accomplish more work with existing capacity. For example, if two or more end-item products require the same purchased component, the owner of the purchasing process could consolidate all requirements for that component into a single purchase order rather than process multiple orders. The consolidation may also result in volume discounts.

In another example, if two approved changes impact the same document and/or the same physical items, they can be consolidated and implemented as one change provided they can share the same effectivity. The affected document, and its associated physical items, can therefore go through the upgrade cycle once instead of twice.

An organization that has a high rate of change will find many opportunities to group approved changes and implement them as a single change. The potential for consolidation depends on their priorities and ability to share the same effectivity. The benefits are proportional to the quantity of shared items and documents that are impacted. Costs of implementing approved changes can be minimized accordingly.

Just-In-Time Principles for Documents

The principles of just-in-time need to be applied to documents similar to the way they are applied to physical items. Physical items are scheduled to arrive just-in-time to support their parent-level applications — whatever the rate of usage happens to be is the rate at which they arrive at the work center where they are used. Higher-cost items are scheduled more closely than lower-cost items.

Just-in-time practices were adopted by Japanese firms long before gaining universal acceptance. The rest of the world was slow to adopt the principles for several reasons. First and foremost, companies did not trust the quality of their materials. They were accustomed to ordering on a just-in-case basis and simply getting another component from the stockroom if one was discovered to be defective.

Furthermore, production activities were usually shortage-driven. Production rates were paced by the ability to clear shortages. Any action that might make shortages worse would be rejected and just-in-time obviously met the criteria.

Another factor was the practice of ordering quantities sufficiently large to last several weeks, if not months. The material scheduling activities used lot-sizing formulas which tried to balance order processing and delivery costs against inventory carrying costs. Those formulas did not include consideration for obsolescence and spoilage that takes place with materials that sit on the shelf.

A parallel can be drawn between materials sitting waiting to be used, and documents sitting in a file waiting to be used. Both exist in a state of change. A document should not be revised today if it is not to be used for several weeks or months. Documents should be updated just-in-time to be used. While such an update is pending, there may be a chance to consolidate multiple changes.

The idea of a just-in-time practice for documents is as scary as when it was first proposed for physical items. In addition to material shortages, downstream activities must work around late releases of engineering drawings. They would resist voting in favor of adopting a just-in-time approach. To make it work, significant improvements in the document release and change processes are in order.

Measurement of Process Maturity

Process maturity is proportional to the degree that an organization has the full range of processes needed to fulfill its goals and the degree to which those processes are reliable and efficient. Whether those processes are weighted toward internal work centers or outside suppliers does not influence the measurement.

The maturity of an organization is a reflection of the maturity of its core business processes. Some will likely be at a higher level of maturity than others. If core business processes are connected like links in a chain, overall organizational maturity might be no better than the "weakest link." On the other hand, core processes could be connected like links in a chain, but if the end-results are influenced like data sets used in-series, overall maturity might be equal to the multiplied sums of their maturity levels.

Although each core business process may contain a network of work centers, each operates like a high-level work center with inputs and outputs. The output of one is the input to another. These interdependencies must be understood before their individual levels of maturity can be translated into a level of maturity for the entire organization.

Another way of determining overall maturity may be more appropriate. As discussed in chapter 3, "when CM works, everything works." Chapter 5, stated that "the reinvented configuration management component provides the infrastructure which enables both project management and quality assurance to be effective." The definitions of CM and CMII as provided in chapter 2 also help to reveal the broader scope of CMII. It may be more meaningful to equate the level of maturity of the entire organization to the level of maturity of the core CMII process.

If and when such a decision is made, measurements to calculate the level of maturity should focus on (1) the ability to accommodate change, (2) the ability to keep requirements clear, concise and valid, (3) reductions in the use of intervention resources, (4) cost reductions derived from reuse and process improvements, and (5) the degree to which documents are updated and released on a just-in-time basis. These measurements can be standardized across industry.

Chapter 11 — Summary

The activities of development are like a job shop environment in that work is accomplished through a network of work centers. Work flows through the network in the form of inputs and outputs. The output of one is the input to another. Inputs must be validated and outputs must be verified. Capacity must be planned and priorities must be controlled.

The goal is to achieve the variety of a job shop along with the reliability, volume and efficiency of a dedicated production line. The techniques were developed by industrial engineers and production control specialists over 30 years ago. Their application, however, generally remains confined to manufacturing. The same techniques are needed in any activity where various types of work are accomplished by various combinations of the same work centers.

No activity is more representative of a job shop environment, or work center network, than the "engineering change" process. No two changes are alike, yet they all flow through various combinations of the same work centers.

Similarly, most engineering change processes are plagued with the same problems commonly found in a job shop environment. One work center can be overloaded with work while another has very little to do. Jobs that have the highest priority move through the entire network rather quickly while others do not move at all. Discrepancies or defects in the product are often detected downstream and not in the work center where they were created. Intervention resources spend an enormous amount of time on expediting and corrective action.

Work center design is all about trust and reliability. Each work center must do everything within its power to assure that jobs are done right. The goal is to build trust that assigned tasks will be accomplished correctly in every case. Reliable standards plus the appropriate skills for applying those standards are key ingredients. Good scheduling and capacity planning techniques are also essential.

Once an organization has adopted CMII, it becomes appropriate to equate the overall level of maturity to the level of maturity of the core CMII process. When CMII works, everything works. Maturity is best measured in terms of CMII process proficiency.

12
CMII-Compliant Enabling Tools

As-planned and as-released baselines must be closely coupled with a closed-loop change process with fast-track capability.

Automation alone does not fix a bad process, but appropriate enabling tools can make a good process much better.

The best tools are those that can enable the full range of CMII functionality and do so in the most user-friendly manner.

To be most user-friendly is to retrieve and display information in desired formats and do so with the fewest number of "clicks."

As-planned and as-released baselines are the cornerstone of the business process infrastructure. The power of the CMII model is derived by integrating such baselines with (1) associated meta-data and repositories, (2) proper owners for each document and data element, (3) appropriate validation and verification techniques, (4) a closed-loop change process with proper decision points, decision rules and fast track capability, (5) scheduling capability, (6) cost estimating capability, (7) appropriate records as a byproduct of each process and (8) appropriate user application skills.

Enabling tools are needed in order to achieve this full range of capabilities in a manner that is truly robust. This chapter describes the functionality that is needed and the priorities for implementation. Criteria used to assess software tools and certify that they are CMII-compliant is also provided.

Paperless Environment: Finally a Reality

A paperless environment became a popular objective in the 1970s but it did not become reality for most organizations until recent years. It remained an elusive goal until a significant percentage of employees had their own personal computers and gradually lost their affinity for paper. A high percentage of today's employees perform their design and administrative tasks on-line. Some organizations are so highly automated that no work can be accomplished when the computers are down. Fear of computers is no longer an obstacle.

The earliest versions of enabling software tools focused on financials and cost accounting. They were physical item-oriented and included the functionality of indentured bills of material. Standard costs were established for each item in those bills. Actual costs were collected and tracked relative to the standard costs. The indentured bills of material were used to "roll-up" and summarize both sets of costs for each end-item product.

The only way those early tools could accommodate documents was to include them in the bills of material. The ability to accommodate documents evolved later, after organizations began using computer-aided design tools and needed a place to store design information. Tools that could merge text with graphics (desktop publishing tools) became available in that same time frame. Today's tools provide the bill of material functionality as well as the ability to link each item at each level to its supporting documents.

It is now possible to retrieve any type of document by simply "clicking" on that document. It is possible to see not only the revisions that have been made to a document but also the authorization for each of those revisions. Users may obtain a copy of any document without knowing where the source copy is located.

Although a paperless environment has become a reality within various industries and government agencies, the functionality provided by current tools is still evolving and user-friendliness is still lacking in most cases. It has become increasingly clear that automation for the sake of automation is not the total answer. Processes must lead and enabling tools must follow. Knowing what the processes need to do has been the missing link.

Out-Of-The-Box Solution: Not There Yet

Developers of software tools must deal with a wide variety of customers and potential customers all of whom have their own terminologies and their own preferences for how work is accomplishcd and what thc cnabling tool should do. It is these differences that cause software developers to focus on organizations in a specific industry or closely-related industries where the magnitude of such differences are less significant.

These diverse needs also prevent software developers from providing a standardized, out-of-the-box solution. Most are forced to provide components of functionality which can be mixed and matched and customized for each customer's application. While one side of the developer's resources are adding components of functionality and striving to improve their integration, the larger side is striving to implement unique combinations of those components of functionality at various customer sites.

Software developers are often surprised to learn their customers are unsure as to what their processes are or what they should be. Customers often assume that no one would develop such tools if they did not understand best industry practices. This is a major reason why buyers may not bother to specify the required functionality; many would not know what to specify if they tried.   They are under the misconception that the software developer knows what they need. The overlooked requirements are exposed when the actual users begin to challenge the functionality. That is when the sparks begin to fly.

As has been stated over and over since computer tools became widely available, the processes must lead and enabling tools must follow. The requirements of the process must drive the functionality of the tools.

Too many organizations spend their money on tools and then try to figure out what their processes should be (which the tools may or may not support). In May 2000, the Institute of Configuration Management began working with the key software developers and helping them understand the functionality needed to support the CMII processes. As of April 1, 2002, eight software products had been certified to be CMII-compliant and several others were in the process.

First Priority: As-Planned and As-Released Baselines

The first priority should be to automate the as-planned and as-released baselines. This is where the most important information used to run the business is established and maintained. The change process, which is closely coupled with such baselines, should follow.

Automation of as-planned and as-released baselines begins with physical item hierarchies and management of the parent-to-child relationships between physical items. The needed functionality must include the ability to link each item at each level to its supporting documentation. Table 12-1 summarizes the information to be included in as-planned and as-released baselines.

> • *End-item model number (or release and version)*
> • *End-item application requirements*
> • *Design basis for the end-item*
> • *Physical item hierarchy (and indenture levels)*
> • *Supporting documents for each item at each level*
> • *ECN authority for each document*
> • *Effectivity for each ECN*
> • *Planned and actual release date for each document*
> • *Items and documents to be superseded*
> • *Superseding items and documents*
> • *Effective date for each document (and item)*

Table 12-1   Content of an as-planned and as-released baseline for a product.

The challenge is to find the most effective way to access and display this information in the most user-friendly manner. This is an area in which enabling tools currently remain underdeveloped. Consideration must be given to how various users can gain access and then navigate to where they need to go.

The potential power of such baselines is derived from how the information sets are linked. Today's tools are able to make the needed linkages, but that is only part of the solution. Ability to access and display the information in a user friendly manner is also essential. The corresponding software must be designed accordingly.

Automation of the Closed-Loop Change Process

The appropriate change process revolves around as-planned and as-released baselines and the associated repositories of documents, data and records. Automating a change process begins with understanding the information to be changed; making the process efficient begins with understanding how the information should be identified, structured, linked and owned.

Figure 12-1 serves to illustrate the interdependencies between a closed-loop change process, baselines and the associated information sets that must be kept synchronized. The effort required to maintain synchronization depends upon how the information sets are identified, linked and displayed.

The best displays are those which prompt the appropriate action. Some linkages are good and some must be avoided. Ability to link things does not mean they should be linked. This is another reason to ensure that processes lead and tools follow.

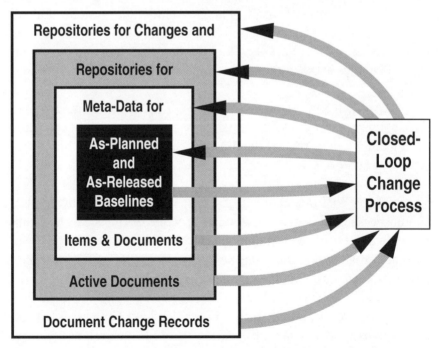

Figure 12-1   Baseline cornerstone with a closely coupled change process.

Work Flow, Terminologies and Ownership

The need for good forms is proportional to the complexity of the process. The forms and the information fields therein must emulate the desired workflow. Good forms can make the most complex process intuitive by making the next step obvious for users. The decision points within a process may cause work to be routed down different paths. Desired work flows must be mapped out and the supporting forms must be designed accordingly.

The CMII model is very specific with regard to the closed-loop change process, the work flow and the decision points therein. The ratio of personnel who use the process relative to those who administer the process can be above 100-to-1. The closed-loop process contains three change administration functions which make the process reliable and efficient for all users.

Another important consideration involves terminologies and common denominators. Implementation of a new system often involves replacing, or interfacing with, one or more existing systems. Field names are rarely consistent across stand-alone systems that are to be replaced. Field names within the new system are not likely to be fully satisfactory to all users either. Reaching an agreement on what the field names and common denominators should be can be a major challenge.

Another important prerequisite for successfully automating the CMII process includes establishing the proper ownership for each design and process-related document. The needed level of integrity cannot be achieved without proper ownership, which is also a prerequisite for processing changes on a fast-track basis.

The CMII model is very specific about how such ownership should be accomplished. A document is never owned by a single individual or by a "department." Every document is co-owned by an assigned creator and at least one designated user. Relatively complex documents are co-owned by a creator and a team of users.

Such provisions for ownership were missing from out-of-the-box software tools until recently. Those that have been assessed and certified to be CMII-compliant now provide such functionality. Robust capability in this area deserves a high priority.

Change Implementation Plans and Execution

The development of detailed implementation plans for approved changes is another area in which enabling tools are needed. Each enterprise change notice has its own implementation plan. These plans need to be constructed in a critical path format. If an initially derived effectivity does not support the urgency of a change, the steps within the critical path will need to be compressed. Project management tools provide such functionality.

Detailed implementation plans for approved changes are developed by a cross-functional team whose members are also responsible for implementation. The development of such plans is a fast-paced activity and preferably accomplished in a face-to-face setting. Individual plans are preferably developed in a work file where the evolving plan can be projected on a screen and made visible to all members. Once an evolving plan is concluded to be satisfactory, it is moved into the master file with other changes already in work.

Once the detailed plan is approved and released, the implementation effort begins immediately. Implementation is a matter of performing each task as planned. Ability to track actual task completions relative to planned completions and make adjustments to resolve unplanned issues is essential, yet it is an area in which every organization struggles. Because the variety and volume of tasks to be managed is simply overwhelming, appropriate enabling tools are sorely needed.

Companies that develop software tools for automating the various facets of the configuration management process are only beginning to focus on the segments where scheduling activities are most comprehensive. Scheduling is such an important part of the configuration management process that the interface between the CM tools and the project management tool needs to be seamless.

The ideal project management tool provides the ability to schedule an entire network of work centers and track all jobs flowing through those work centers relative to their schedules. The ideal tool can provide visibility of workloads at each work center in each time period. It can also display actual progress relative to plan in such a way that a need for corrective action is readily visible.

Criteria for Assessing and Certifying Software Tools

Enabling software tools are assessed against 23 sets of criteria (see Table 12-2). Requirements 1 through 8 provide the infrastructure for the change process. Requirements 9 through 17 contain the key elements of the change process. Requirements 18 through 23 focus on followthrough activities. A current listing of software tools certified to be CMII-compliant is provided on the Institute of Configuration Management website at www.icmhq.com.

1　As-planned and as-released baseline
2　Terminologies
3　Lowest common denominators
4　Naming and numbering conventions
5　Model number and release/version number
6　Hierarchies and item-to-document linkages
7　Document identification and ownership
8　One set of priorities for development
9　Closed-loop change process
10　Change forms and logs
11　CRB and CIB (for complex changes)
12　Change administration I, II and III
13　Fast track option (for low risk changes)
14　Change cost estimates
15　One ECN for many ECRs and vice versa
16　Detailed ECN implementation planning
17　Change effectivities
18　Change and revision records
19　Supply chain management
20　Work authorizations
21　As-built records
22　Support of O&M and O&R
23　Schedule and cost performance

Table 12-2　Assessment check list for certifying CMII-compliant tools.

The Meaning of CMII-Compliant Certification

The assessment and certification of software tools was initiated by the Institute of Configuration Management for two reasons: (1) to help software developers improve the functionality of their enabling tools and (2) to help CMII-trained professionals find software that can best support their efforts to implement the CMII process in their respective environments. Table 12-3 describes what it means when a tool is certified to be CMII-compliant.

- *Although it may not be robust, the software is capable of providing the core CMII functionality per requirements 1 through 7.*

- *The software has the potential to be robust in all areas of functionality as needed by the users of such a tool.*

- *The software developer understands and agrees with its strengths and weaknesses as derived from the assessment.*

- *The software developer plans to make improvements which will build upon its strengths and overcome its weaknesses.*

- *The Institute of Configuration Management agrees with the developer's priorities for making those improvements.*

- *Each certification shall remain in effect as long as users (our mutual customers) are satisfied that the software is evolving as planned.*

Table 12-3   CMII-compliant software and meaning of certification by ICM.

It is important to note that the concept of as-planned and as-released baselines is relatively new to the providers of software tools. Most software tools assessed to date have the various components of functionality needed to support such baselines but there is still an issue regarding how such information is retrieved and displayed.

This is an area in which significant improvement is needed across the entire population of software tools. Fortunately, it is one in which the developers whose tools have been certified are now focused. The users of those tools should expect to see major improvements in the near future.

Chapter 12 — Summary

Enabling tools are needed in order to achieve the appropriate business process infrastructure. Although a paperless environment has become a reality in most industries and government agencies, the functionality provided by current tools is still evolving and user-friendliness is still lacking in most cases. In May 2000, the Institute of Configuration Management began helping software developers understand the functionality needed to support the CMII processes.

The first priority should be to automate the as-planned and as-released baselines. This is where the most important information used to run the business is established and maintained. The change process, which is closely coupled with such baselines, should follow.

The appropriate change process revolves around as-planned and as-released baselines and the associated repositories. Automating a change process begins with understanding the information to be changed; making the process efficient begins with understanding how the information should be identified, structured, linked and owned.

Another important consideration involves terminologies and common denominators. Field names are rarely consistent across stand-alone systems that are to be replaced. Reaching agreement on what the field names and common denominators should be can be a major challenge.

Another critical step is to establish the proper ownership for each design and process-related document. The CMII model is very specific about how such ownership should be accomplished. Tools that have been assessed and certified now provide such functionality.

The process of developing detailed change implementation plans is another area in which enabling tools are needed. Project management tools that can support the development of schedules in a critical-path format are essential. The interfaces with such scheduling tools need to be seamless.

The Institute of Configuration Management assesses and certifies software tools as a way to help developers improve their functionality and thereby enhance the ability of users to implement the CMII process. As of April 1, 2002, eight tools had been certified to be CMII-compliant.

13

CMII Implementation and ROI

To upgrade any complex process or system involves a
preparation phase, a transition phase and an application phase.

The preparation phase serves to define the destination
and provide a transition plan for how to get there.

Root causes for any failures reside in the preparation phase.
Return-on-investment is achieved in the application phase.

Initial benefits appear in the form of reduced corrective action.
Benefits thereafter appear in the form of real improvements.

Any business process improvement effort that is not accomplished in a "top-down" fashion is not likely to succeed. Top-down means that the effort is being driven by upper management. It means that all activities are pulling in the same direction to achieve one common goal.

Although a top-down approach is highly preferred, it is not fail-safe. The success rate for implementing complex systems is not good. That should not be the case. Unsuccessful implementations are not accidents, they are caused.

This chapter describes a three-phase process for implementing CMII that include preparation, transition and application. The steps within each phase are described along with the return-on-investment that should be expected. The initial steps are building blocks for those that follow.

Preparation Phase and Cross-Functional Teams

The initial phase of any process improvement and/or system implementation effort involves preparation. The first step is to define the destination in terms of preferred practices and enabling tools. The next step is to develop a plan for how to transition from existing practices and tools to the preferred practices and tools.

The preparation effort within a larger organization will be most successful if it is accomplished by two cross-functional teams. A higher-level team represents a steering committee whose members are comprised of upper levels of management such as vice presidents, directors and/or managers. The role of the steering committee is to provide direction, approve plans, make major business decisions and provide support as needed. The steering committee is also responsible for ensuring that other members of top management are kept apprised of implementation progress and status.

The members of the subordinate-level team generally report to the steering committee members and are directly involved in leading and coordinating the day-to-day effort. The members of the subordinate-level team are responsible for preparing plans, obtaining approvals, coordinating implementation, problem resolution, plan maintenance and progress reports.

Relatively small organizations do not need two teams if one team can perform both roles. In that case, the president might serve in the role of the steering committee.

The number of members on the subordinate-level team and their selection are important considerations. There is a trade-off between proper representation and team size. Ensuring that each activity is properly represented tends to add members. Smaller teams, however, move faster than large teams. The ideal team is comprised of the fewest members than can effectively represent all activities.

Selecting the appropriate chairperson is also a key consideration. The ideal candidate must be a good facilitator and should not have voting rights as other team members do. The chairperson is responsible for coordinating all team meetings, providing the agenda and distributing minutes, as well as providing progress reports to the steering committee.

Define Destination by Tailoring the CMII Model

To define the destination associated with any process improvement and/or system implementation effort is to define the preferred practices that will be in place once the destination is reached. To define the destination associated with implementation of CMII is to define the business process infrastructure and preferred practices that will be in place once the plan is achieved.

Statistics compiled by the Institute of Configuration Management show that the lack of a clear, concise and valid destination is the leading cause of implementation failures precisely because this first step provides the foundation for the next step and all steps which follow. Understanding what the better processes and tools *should be* is an aspect that is usually underdeveloped because it is difficult to sort through the issues and their interdependencies and reach agreement about what the ultimate solution should be in any level of detail. Organizations simply march ahead and try to "build bridges as they discover rivers."

The CMII model, which has been in a state of evolution since 1986, serves to define the appropriate destination. The issues and interdependencies associated with the desired destination are dissected and reassembled by every group of professionals that go through the courses required to achieve certification. The CMII model provides the ideal template to stake out the destination that most organizations are unable to develop on their own.

Any organization that wishes to improve its business process infrastructure should begin by creating its own tailored version of the CMII model. Such tailoring is best accomplished by the cross-functional implementation team. The tailored version is then reviewed and approved by the steering committee.

Once all parties agree on the destination, it is then possible to proceed to the next step. The agreed upon destination provides the basis for assessing existing practices and developing a transition plan. Again, proper closure must be brought to this first step before proceeding to the next step. This first step, if properly completed, is where implementations begin to succeed. It is also where implementations begin to fail if not completed properly.

Team Member Selection and Training

The appropriate steering committee is an executive-level committee comprised of the fewest number of officers, vice presidents and/or directors capable of representing all of top management. To ensure success, the selected members must have a sincere interest in the implementation effort, participating not only in the planning phase but also supporting each implementation step thereafter.

The steering committee is responsible for identifying the core business processes that will be used to run the business once the desired destination is achieved. It also falls to committee members to identify the owners of as-planned core processes relative to the existing core processes — all ideal candidates for the implementation team.

The steering committee must ensure that each member of the implementation team is properly trained, however, appropriate guidance cannot be provided until its own members are well versed in CMII. The appropriate guidance cannot be provided by the steering committee until its own members are properly trained. Probability of success will be optimized if each member of each team completes the training required for CMII certification.

There are options for receiving training, each with distinct advantages. Bringing the required courses on-site minimizes the training costs and allows team members to participate in group discussions and gain a common understanding of the destination relative to existing practices.

Another option is to attend public courses and learn from students from diverse industries as well as government agencies. Public sessions provide a unique opportunity to discuss the full myriad of problems and solutions from many points of view. Students soon discover their problems are not unique and the appropriate solutions are essentially the same.

Training additional personnel is relatively easy to sort out and can be addressed later, but for now must remain on the two cross-functional teams involved in the preparation phase. The number of members on each team is preferably the fewest that are capable of representing the entire organization.

Assessment of Existing Processes and Tools

A business process improvement plan is derived from an assessment of existing processes and tools relative to those which are preferred. A top-down approach is recommended for subdividing an assessment into manageable and meaningful increments.

For improvement planning purposes, the business process infrastructure is subdivided into categories 1 through 5 as shown in Table 13-1. A top-down approach is achieved by beginning with category 1 and assessing each category in the sequence as shown. The assessments within each category must focus on processes first and enabling tools second. The strengths and weaknesses of the processes and the tools should both be understood when finished.

1   Administrative Hierarchy, Business Enterprise
2   Physical Item Hierarchies, Research & Development
3   Naming, Numbering and Reuse
4   Validation and Release Records
5   Changes and Revision Records
6   Systems and Enabling Tools

Table 13-1   Six categories for business process infrastructure assessment.

Each requirement within each of the six categories is stated on a separate assessment form. The requirement is stated in one field. Enabling tools needed to accomplish the requirement, if any, are identified in a second field. Strengths and weaknesses of the existing processes are stated in a third field. A fourth field addresses the capabilities of existing tools. A fifth field defines the impact and/or risk associated with any deficiencies that are noted.

Assessments should be divided into appropriate phases. The first phase may obtain enough information to implement the first module. Each phase may obtain additional information with which to implement additional modules. At each phase, major gaps may need to be resolved before proceeding to the next.

Development of a Transition Plan

The transition plan is derived from the results of the assessment. Transition plans are subdivided into major phases. Major phases are generally subdivided into smaller phases and there can be extensive overlap between the many phases. Each detailed plan is created on a just-in-time basis and some are being created as others are being completed.

The transition phases are comprised of modules which can be prototyped first and then moved into production in a building-block fashion and on a program-by-program basis. The sequence for prototyping and implementation will be similar to the assessment phases and/or categories shown in Table 13-1. To avoid excessive work-arounds, modules which are highly interdependent must be implemented together.

From a timing point of view, it is appropriate to equate the implementation of one or more modules to steps in a staircase. If all modules could be implemented at once, there would be no need for work-arounds. To implement another set of modules is to take one more step up the staircase. Each step introduces a new set of work-arounds. The best transition plan is one that accomplishes the prototyping and implementation phases with minimum work-arounds.

There is extensive overlap between all three implementation phases, preparation, transition and application. Since each detailed plan is created on a just-in-time basis, the next steps are being planned as previous steps are being completed. Situations will change. Unplanned events will occur. The overall plan must be kept current.

Required work-arounds should be identified to the degree that they are known and included in the transition plan. Each transition phase, once initiated, should be taken quickly and, once completed, allowed to settle in before proceeding to the next step. A steady pace is preferred.

The probability of implementation success is greatly enhanced if the members of both cross-functional teams can remain in place throughout the entire effort. This should be one of the key criteria used to select the team members. Anyone with limited durability or staying power should not selected as a team member.

Implementation Steps and Levels of Proficiency

Full implementation of the CMII model is achieved in 8 steps as shown in Figure 13-1. The destination is established in step 1. The assessment is completed and the high-level transition plan is created in step 2. Steps 3-8 support the transition and application phases.

An organization that takes all 8 steps transitions through 5 levels of proficiency. Those with no plan are at level 1. They reach level 2 once a plan is established, level 3 once the plan is proofed and implemented on the first business program, level 4 when corrective action is cut in half and level 5 once it is eliminated.

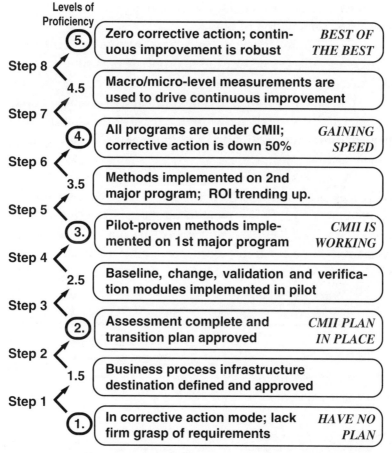

Figure 13-1   CMII: eight implementation steps and five levels of proficiency.

Cost Avoidance Versus Cost Reduction

The benefits to be derived by improving proficiency are measurable, and will appear in two forms. One is realized in terms of reduced corrective action, the other in terms of real improvements. Reduced corrective action will lead and real improvements will follow. Statistics compiled by the Institute of Configuration Management have shown that real improvements will accelerate as corrective action continues to decline.

Real improvements come in many forms. An action that improves a design is one example. To improve a process that already works as it should is also a real improvement. An improvement that reduces cost, however, could be a cost avoidance or a real improvement, or a combination of both.

The differences between cost avoidance and cost reduction must be understood before the appropriate measurements can be established. Just as continuous corrective action is not continuous improvement, cost avoidance is not the same as cost reduction. The example in Table 13-2 shows how cost avoidance can be distinguished from cost reduction and how the benefits should be calculated in each case.

A process was consuming 20 resource units and producing 100 pieces per hour, of which 10 were defective. An additional 5 resource units were being spent to fix the 10 defective pieces. The process, as improved, consumes just 10 units of resources and produces 100 defect-free pieces per hour. The amount of cost avoidance is 5 resource units per hour, while the cost reduction is 11 (1 + 10) resource units per hour.

	Process before	Process after	Cost avoidance	Cost reduction
Good pieces/hour:	90	100	-	$\frac{+\ net\ 10}{10} = 1$
Defective pieces/hour:	10	0	-	-
First time resources:	20	10	-	10
Intervention resources:	5	0	5	-

Table 13-2   Calculation of cost avoidance and cost reduction.

Projected Return-on-Investment

Figure 13-2 shows how the return-on-investment from implementing CMII starts out negative and turns positive. Although return-on-investment remains negative through the fourth implementation step, it begins a positive trend thereafter, becoming increasingly robust throughout steps 6, 7 and 8.

The implementation time frame will vary according to the quality of the preparation phase and the level of effort. Although return-on-investment is achieved in the application phase, its magnitude is highly dependent upon the quality of the preparation phase (implementation steps 1 and 2).

Like any development effort, the initial steps are most important because that is where a development project is given its best chance to succeed. To accept a weak preparation phase is to be put into a position of depending upon heroics in later phases. The real heros are those who do the job right during the preparation phase.

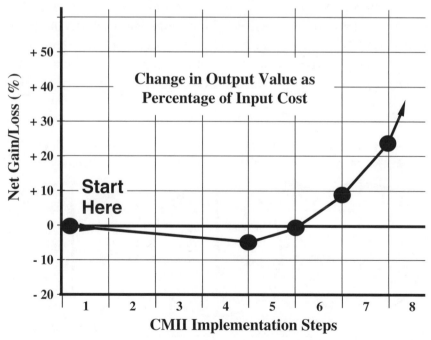

Figure 13-2   Return-on-investment relative to implementation steps.

First Priority: Eliminate Corrective Action

Corrective action is an invisible monster that inflates cost of sales and erodes profits. It can create a tremendous amount of havoc, yet the root causes are not easy to detect. The need for corrective action most often stems from seemingly unimportant issues.

They can range from an error in a drawing, to an error in a line of code, to an error in a referenced table. A large percentage of errors may appear to be very minor when reviewed independently of all other errors; however, what is not readily visible is the magnitude of their impact as they come together.

As stated in chapter 9, statistics compiled by the Institute of Configuration Management reveal that most organizations spend 40 to 60% of their resources on corrective action. The three pie charts in Figure 13-3 show how profitability improves with reductions in corrective action. The pie chart on the left is a starting point showing close to 40% of resources being spent on corrective action.

An organization that achieves proficiency level 2 is beginning to make an impact on corrective action. Proficiency level 4 is achieved once corrective action is cut in half — profitability has more than doubled at that point. At proficiency level 5, corrective action has been virtually eliminated and real improvements have become highly robust. The real bottom line is, of course, that profitability has also become truly robust.

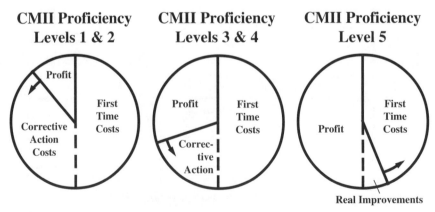

| CMII Proficiency Levels 1 & 2 | CMII Proficiency Levels 3 & 4 | CMII Proficiency Level 5 |

Figure 13-3   Profitability relative to levels of proficiency.

Maquiladora Industry and Offshore Manufacturing

During the 1960s, American firms were rapidly increasing offshore assembly activity in the Far East. In 1965, Mexico initiated a similar "border industrialization program" known as the maquiladora industry. (A *maquiladora* is an assembly plant). The program is also called the "in-bond industry" since goods are shipped "in-bond" from the United States to Mexico and back.

As of 1995, there were 2,136 assembly plants near the US-Mexico border with nearly half a million employees. About 65% of those plants and 80% of the employees were part of the electronics industry. These plants are highly attractive to American firms because labor rates in Mexico are a fraction of those in the states.

Unfortunately, environmental problems have also surged as maquiladora plants have multiplied. The environmental laws and the infrastructure for handling wastes are both very weak. In 1995, Mexican authorities asserted that 25% of all hazardous wastes could not be accounted for.

The important point is that too many U.S. firms are striving to reduce the direct labor component of their total costs (only 5% of total costs per Figure 13-4) while doing far too little about the other 95%. Those that focus on reducing corrective action will achieve much better results. This recommendation also applies to companies that are going offshore for software development.

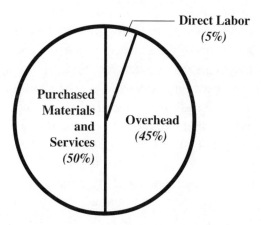

Figure 13-4   Typical cost ratios for a job shop-oriented manufacturing facility.

Chapter 13 — Summary

The upgrade of any complex process and/or system involves a preparation phase, a transition phase and an application phase. The preparation phase defines the destination and provides a transition plan for how to get there. Return-on-investment is achieved in the application phase. The best chance to succeed is provided in the preparation phase. This is also where implementations that fall short of expectations first go off track.

Full implementation of the CMII model is achieved in eight steps. The destination is established in step 1. The assessment and the high-level transition plan are established in step 2. The transition and application phases are achieved with steps 3 through 8.

An organization that completes all eight steps transitions from proficiency level 1 to level 5. Those with no plan are at level 1. Level 2 is reached once there is an approved plan, level 3 once the plan is implemented on the first business program, level 4 when the plan is implemented on all programs and intervention resources are cut in half, and level 5 when intervention resources are reduced to zero and real improvements are robust.

The CMII model defines the appropriate destination which most organizations are unable to develop on their own. It provides the ideal template which any organization can tailor and thereby create its own destination.

A transition plan is a step-by-step plan for how to transition from existing processes and enabling tools to the preferred processes and tools. Definition of the existing processes and tools, and their strengths and weaknesses, are derived by assessing them relative to the preferred processes and tools.

The transition plan is comprised of modules which can be prototyped first and then moved into production in a building-block fashion. To avoid excessive work-arounds, modules which are highly interdependent must be implemented together.

Return-on-investment from implementing CMII starts out negative and turns positive. It remains negative through the fourth implementation step and turns positive thereafter. ROI becomes increasingly robust throughout steps 6, 7 and 8.

14

How to Get Started

*Organizations gain fame through their products but
trust and respect is earned through their processes.*

*Great products are byproducts of good processes. Insiders
know it is the processes that should be in the showcase.*

*Insiders know their processes are their competitive weapon.
How to keep them truly robust, however, is the challenge.*

*CMII professionals know the infrastructure which enables the
processes is most important of all. Therein lies the secret.*

Getting started begins with knowing the destination and why anyone should want to go there. Determining how to get there begins with knowing where you are and why anyone should want to leave. Such moves are not easy — it is just too much trouble unless there is something really great to look forward to.

A top-down approach, as described in the previous chapter, is one way to get started but strong interest and support from upper management is a prerequisite. A bottom-up approach can also be a viable option when such support is lacking.

Beginning the journey does not mean that the destination must be known in finite detail. However, the general direction and the major obstacles to be resolved must be understood. This chapter describes some of the alternatives for getting started and how to build momentum and support along the way.

Start With This Book

This book has described the proper destination and how to get there, and has made clear why all parties should want to go there. It is a place where intervention resources are not needed since there is no corrective action. It is a place where changes can be accommodated and requirements kept clear, concise and valid.

This book has also described the conditions in which most organizations currently operate. The majority are suffocating on corrective action, forcing an inordinate percentage of all resources to continually perform heroics to rescue quality and schedules. As we have seen, such rescues are not always successful despite the high price paid. This book has established why no one should want to continue operating in such an environment.

This book has also made it clear that automation is only part of the answer. Automation can make a good process better but it cannot, in itself, fix a bad process; that begins with fixing the infrastructure enabling those processes. This book has detailed the appropriate infrastructure.

A deeper investigation revealed that the magic resides in the infrastructure. Invaluable nuggets of wisdom have remained hidden there because they look, feel and sound too much like configuration management. This book has brought the underlying principles out into the open and made them visible. Those principles were then consolidated, realigned and integrated with the principles of project management and quality assurance. The result is called CMII.

The CMII model has been established as the proper destination. Any organization can create its own tailored version of that model. Any organization can assess its existing processes and tools against that destination and establish the appropriate transition plan.

To get started boils down to determining if such a destination represents a better place to be. It includes gaining confidence that the benefits of being there will outweigh the cost of getting there, in addition to considering other alternatives that may be attractive.

Regardless of the alternative selected, this book has shown that CM is a process which enables all other processes. When CM works, everything works. When CM is not working, nothing works.

Required Resources Already Exist

To embark on any business process improvement initiative requires the appropriate authorization and justifying the required time and resources which may, or may not, be readily available. One or more process improvement initiatives may already be initiated so it becomes a matter of priority. The top executive certainly has a strong vote in what the priorities should be. It becomes a matter of comparing the costs versus benefits of each initiative and the degree to which the required resources are available in each case.

Before going deeper into the authorization issue, it is appropriate to consider who should lead and coordinate a process improvement effort such as CMII. It is logical that all elements of CM should be brought together under one manager. It also makes sense that these same elements should be integrated into the core CMII process. Once done, it becomes obvious that the owner of the core CMII process should lead the CMII implementation effort.

Logically, the owners of the other core business processes should validate the CMII implementation plans and verify the results because each is enabled by the CM process. When CM works properly, all other core business processes work properly.

This is where the resource issue must be addressed. The costs of implementing CMII are generally incurred within the core CMII process but the major benefits are found outside CM. In fact, the savings outside CM justify the costs of implementing CMII. Furthermore, the resources needed to implement CMII are only a fraction of what is currently being spent on intervention.

It must also be recognized, however, that those most deeply involved in corrective action generally perceive CM as the problem, not the solution. This is why most business process improvement initiatives focus on everything but CM. Once it is understood that the solutions reside in CM, the right priorities become obvious.

The role of upper management is clear: Establish CMII as a core business process, redirect existing resources, assign core process owners and empower them to implement CMII. The owners of the core business processes should lead the effort. The required resources already exist.

Core Business Process Owners and Training

The owners of the core business processes are the most important players in any organization — and particularly in any business process improvement initiative. An organization that has not bothered to identify its core business processes and assign appropriate owners will never be as competitive as those that do. It will unlikely have the right players involved in the improvement initiatives that already exist.

The idea that companies should organize around their business processes is not new. That idea became most prominent during the peak of the total quality management crusade. The concept of empowering employees came out of that movement. The idea was right but the how-to was missing. Assuming that empowered employees do not need leadership was wrong, as was discarding organizational charts or turning them upside down.

The core processes used to run the business must be clearly identified. Appropriate owners must be assigned and empowered to ensure their process is reliable and efficient. Each owner must also be given responsibility for continuously improving reliability and efficiency.

CMII must also be established as one of those core business processes. This is the essential piece that has been missing — the piece that empowers all employees, from the top to the bottom of the organizational hierarchy, as creators and/or users. It is CMII that provides the ability to accommodate change, ensures each document is clear, concise and valid, and ensures that each database is 100% accurate.

When considering CMII training, the owners of the core business processes deserve the highest priority. They are in the best position to upgrade existing processes and apply the principles as well as determine the extent of additional training.

Upper management needs CMII training to the degree that their understanding and support is needed and should be provided during the preparation phase. Individuals subordinate to the core process owners need training on how to apply the principles and should be provided during the transition and application phases.

Easier to Be Forgiven Than to Obtain Permission

Approximately two-thirds of all CMII implementation efforts to date are being pursued in a bottom-up manner. Most individuals involved in such approaches have taken turns trying to gain upper management's interest and support. Too often, those most directly involved in configuration management activities find upper management does not understand what they do or why they do it. (Some upper-level managers are known to run the other way when they hear anything that sounds like "CM").

People often use the expression "easier said than done" when something represents a challenge. Configuration management professionals are known to use that expression in reverse — they prefer to say "easier done than said." Many have adopted the Nike slogan "Just do it" as their motto. They often find it easier to be forgiven than to obtain permission.

Wishful thinking notwithstanding, upper management cannot be neglected when training is being planned. It is important that they understand the destination and the transition plan, and equally important that they recognize the significance of the core business processes and the roles its owners must play. Furthermore, it is essential they understand their own roles in CMII implementation and how those roles should change as the transition takes place.

This brings forth another observation. It is common knowledge that the salaries and compensation awarded to top-level executives, such as vice presidents, are intended to be commensurate with their value and contributions to the organization. There was a time when the vice president of engineering ranked highest; the VPs of operations, sales, human resources and finance have all taken their turns as well.

Which executive position will rank the highest once all activities are fully compliant with the CMII model? Within which executive area should the core CMII process reside? What should that position be called? Which of the existing executive positions is best suited to lead the CMII implementation effort? There are no firm answers as CMII is still in its infancy. Appropriate answers will be forthcoming as organizations begin to operate in the CMII mode.

Note: Executive Position to Be Filled

Organizations that reach the CMII destination will discover their previous organizational alignment was awkward and inadequate. They will also find, if they actually reach the destination, that the needed realignment should have been made back when the implementation effort was initiated.

Each organization will need to go through a learning curve before the proper alignment can be sorted out. This is new ground. Very few companies have already reached the point where they were able to escape the corrective action mode. Those who have escaped will not want to be benchmarked, preferring to avoid the risk their secrets might be passed on to their competitors. This book has revealed part of their story but not all of it.

Certain observations will be made sooner or later as organizations march toward the CMII destination. They can be reduced to choices: Which would you rather have, a highly creative individual working with a poor process or someone with average skills working with a good process? What would the answer be if there were ten, or a hundred, or a thousand individuals working with that same process? Would the answer differ from discipline to discipline?

The power will shift to the individuals who are best at managing processes. It will go to those who excel at integrating all processes into one cohesive unit and making that common process reliable and efficient for all users, regardless of the activity in which they reside. There is no existing executive position in today's organizational hierarchies which has such a broad, and yet focused, responsibility.

This is the position that needs to be filled. It is the ideal position, both to lead the CMII implementation effort and oversee the core CMII process once the destination is reached. The job position requires a set of skills not commonly sought by executive search firms. It is not that the skills do not exist, but rather, the opportunity to apply those skills and hone them into perfection had not previously existed. That opportunity has arrived, but an appropriate name for the position has yet to be determined. The CMII principles will survive whether the name survives or not.

Progress, Cost and Benefit Measurements

From a CMII perspective, the potential for reducing operating costs is enormous — but then so is the potential for increasing revenues when an organization is not suffocating on correction action. Financial reports have never revealed the degree to which corrective action has consumed resources. Activity-based cost accounting was a good idea but it is not getting the job done. Measuring the cost of quality was a good idea but it misses the target too. Today's organizations simply do not have a handle on their real cost drivers. Obviously, better measurements are essential.

The appropriate macro-level measurements must be put into place. The primary focus of existing measurements in most organizations revolve around revenues, operating costs and profit. Such financial-oriented measurements are highly standardized because they are both required and regulated. Although "cost of quality" is often a line item within reported operating costs, overall cost measurements do not reveal what is really going on.

In far too many cases, the most important macro-level measurement is missing. Due to the absence of specific measurements, organizations are shielded from the magnitude of the resources being spent on corrective action. They do not understand this powerful force that plays havoc with their bottom line.

This macro-level measurement needs to be firmly in place at the time the CMII implementation effort is initiated and continue after the destination has been achieved. It reveals the true health of the organization by providing the best single indicator of real benefits being achieved. Organizations are, otherwise, running blind.

Micro-level measurements are temporary. They are initiated when the macro-level measurements reveal a problem or a need for improvement. Micro-level measurements are used to identify root causes and to select the best alternative for resolution. They are discontinued once the selected solution is implemented.

Any organization that can "change faster and document better" has a distinct advantage over its competitors. Both parameters must be monitored. The magnitude of the resources spent on intervention in each period is a subset of those measurements.

Consideration for Enabling Tools

Processes must lead; tools must enable. Consideration for enabling tools must come after the desired processes have been defined, and after the infrastructure has been defined, documented, validated and released. Any effort to select a tool before then is premature.

Although enabling software tools are readily available to support many of the process components, there are still numerous applications for which existing software tools are not highly robust. As-planned and as-released baselines top of the list of processes for which off-the-shelf software is most underdeveloped.

Existing tools are able to provide hierarchal relationships and link various items to their associated information sets. In fact, most modern tools provide highly effective capability in this regard. The major deficiencies are basically "user friendliness" issues regarding how information is accessed, organized and displayed. Excessive key strokes are typically required to gain access to the individual data sets. What's more, it is often difficult to bring the various data sets together and display them in a manner that makes the most sense to users.

Another area that needs to be addressed revolves around terminologies. Existing field names are often inconsistent with the CMII terminologies, but several tool providers are now making a concerted effort to adopt them. In some cases, though, field names are so highly embedded that a change will require a major redesign.

Tools with work flow capability are needed to automate the closed-loop change process. Scheduling tools that can drive requirements for subordinate level items through indentured bills of material are needed to drive all development resources with one set of priorities. Tools with project management capability are needed to develop detailed change implementation plans in a critical path format. Those same tools, if sufficiently robust, can provide change task tracking, capacity planning and priority control capabilities as needed.

CMII involves a wide range of functionality which goes far beyond the capabilities of a single tool. It is necessary to select tools with specific types of functionality that can be integrated into one cohesive unit. Just remember; processes must lead, tools enable.

CMII Skills and Supply Versus Demand

The CMII model and the associated training places a tremendous emphasis on processes and the skills of process administrators. The closed-loop change process contains three process administrators called "change administrators." Change administration I handles the analysis phase. Change administration II manages the implementation phase. Change administration III deals with the validation and release phase.

Change administration I and II require the skills of a program manager. Change administration III requires the skills of an auditor. These three functions are the key to process reliability and efficiency, ensuring it works for all users throughout the entire organization. All three focus on accommodating change and keeping requirements clear, concise and valid (which includes synchronization). All three report to the core CMII process owner.

Key decision points within the closed-loop change process are clearly identified. Ability to make the appropriate decisions becomes relatively easy when costs and benefits are clearly identified — and when work loads versus capacity are clearly visible. The change administrators are skilled in making the appropriate information available at each point where a business decision is required.

The demand for CMII skills has experienced steady growth for several years and has accelerated over the past four years. Much of this growth is being driven by companies that have adopted CMII as their corporate standard. Some is being driven by software companies that provide enabling tools. More and more help-wanted ads for configuration management personnel state a preference for those with CMII certification.

The Institute of Configuration Management has attempted, on behalf of industry, to get universities to include a CMII course as an elective, if not a requirement, in undergraduate or advanced degree curriculums. Those efforts have not been successful because too few university administrators and professors recognize the nuggets of wisdom that reside within the CM principles, and they have had no exposure to CMII. This will change as the demand from industry continues to grow.

Chapter 14 — Summary

The CMII model has been established as the proper destination. Any organization can create their own tailored version of that model. Any organization can assess their existing processes and tools against that destination and establish the appropriate transition plan.

The costs to implement CMII are incurred within the core CMII process but the benefits are derived outside CM. The cost savings outside CM more than justify the costs required to implement CMII. Furthermore, the resources required to implement CMII are only a fraction of those being spent on intervention. This is why the resources required to implement CMII already exist.

The CMII model and the associated training places tremendous emphasis on processes and the skills of process administrators. The closed-loop change process contains three change administrators. One handles the analysis phase, one the implementation phase and the third handles the validation and release phase. Two require the skills of a program manager and one requires the skills of an auditor.

The three combined, are the key to process reliability and efficiency. They make the process work for all users. All three report to the core CMII process owner and focus on accommodating change and keeping requirements clear, concise and valid.

The appropriate macro-level measurements must be put into place and used to monitor implementation progress, costs, benefits and intervention resources. The measurement of intervention resources is new and an excellent indicator of real progress.

Consideration for enabling tools must come after the desired processes and business process infrastructure have been defined, documented, validated and released. Any effort to select a tool before then is premature.

The demand for CMII skills has experienced steady growth for several years and has accelerated over the past four years. Much of this growth is driven by companies that have adopted CMII as their corporate standard. More and more want ads for configuration management personnel state a preference for those with CMII certification. Universities are not yet ready to add a CMII course to their degree curriculums but this will change as the demand grows.

Source for CMII Training

The Institute of Configuration Management is the only source for CMII training and certification. Certification is achieved by satisfactorily completing Courses I through VI.

This six-course series is currently conducted in a public format at least once a year in several major cities. Organizations with many personnel to train may choose to bring the courses on-site.

These courses are sponsored by Arizona State University and the University of Tennessee.

Profile of Courses Currently Offered

Required for CMII Certification

I. Configuration Management & the CMII Model

II. Structured Configuration and Process Information

III. Key Elements of Change Management

IV. Closed-Loop and Fast Track Change Process

V. CMII Operating Standards & Legal Liabilities

VI. CMII Assessment, Implementation & Application

VII. Software Development With CMII

VIII. Software CM Process Improvement

IX. Update and Refresher for CMII Grads

X. CMII Awareness

XII. CMII Principles and Tailored Application

(For abstracts, outlines, locations, schedules, fees, etc., go to www.icmhq.com)

Institute of Configuration Management
PO Box 5656, Scottsdale, AZ 85261
(480) 998-8600 Phone — (480) 998-8923 FAX — www.icmhq.com

List of Figures

Figure 2-1   *Communicate formally via documents, data, forms and records.*

Figure 2-2   *Stand-alone systems: byproduct of stove-pipe processes.*

Figure 4-1   *Shewhart (or Deming) cycle for project management.*

Figure 4-2   *Dual-cycle project management per CMII.*

Figure 4-3   *V-diagram of development: design top-down, build bottom-up.*

Figure 4-4   *Closed-loop change process closely coupled with baselines.*

Figure 5-1   *Products and services: a trade-off between needs and capabilities.*

Figure 5-2   *A requirements-driven organization works to released documents.*

Figure 5-3   *Overall scope and emphasis of CMII.*

Figure 5-4   *Corrective action and root causes.*

Figure 5-5   *Factors which influence quality of life in the work place.*

Figure 5-6   *Intervention resources used to rescue quality & schedule.*

Figure 5-7   *Configuration management activities under one umbrella.*

Figure 5-8   *Functional schematic of the CMII model.*

Figure 6-1   *Hierarchy of administrative requirements for a business enterprise.*

Figure 7-1   *Relationships between forms, documents, items and records.*

Figure 8-1   *9-digit item identification number that includes a dash number.*

Figure 8-2   *9-digit significant number for a like-family of flat washers.*

Figure 8-3   *Example of a model number.*

Figure 8-4   *Example of convention used to identify commercial software.*

Figure 8-5   *Example of convention used to identify source code files.*

Figure 9-1   *Organizational performance as a function of data integrity.*

Figure 9-2   *Planning bills for scheduling physical item receipts and issues.*

Figure 12-1 *Baseline cornerstone with a closely coupled change process.*

Figure 13-1 *CMII: eight implementation steps and five levels of proficiency.*

Figure 13-2 *Return-on-investment relative to implementation steps.*

Figure 13-3 *Profitability relative to levels of proficiency.*

Figure 13-4 *Typical cost ratios for a job shop-oriented manufacturing facility.*

List of Tables

Table 2-1   Traditional definition of configuration management.

Table 2-2   Definition of CM and CMII.

Table 3-1   CMII operating guidelines and/or rules.

Table 3-2   Statistics on software development in the U.S. for 1995.

Table 3-3   Motor vehicle division computer system development fiasco.

Table 3-4   Difficulty experienced by the FBI in retrieving records.

Table 3-5   Air traffic control system requirements and change management.

Table 3-6   Difficulty with the Titan IV rocket and its reliability.

Table 3-7   Process improvement with zero work-loss incidents as the driver.

Table 3-8   Development where design leads and software products conform.

Table 3-9   Software development and the power of process.

Table 3-10   Examples of benefits derived from software process improvement.

Table 4-1   Examples of help-wanted advertisements for data managers.

Table 4-2   Examples of help-wanted advertisements for records management.

Table 4-3   Example of a help-wanted ad for a document control clerk.

Table 4-4   Example of a help-wanted advertisement for a librarian.

Table 6-1   Hierarchy of administrative requirements for a business enterprise.

Table 10-1   Development process.

Table 10-2   Planned versus evolutionary approach to development.

Table 10-3   Steps to rescue a troubled software development project.

Table 11-1   A good vision plus ability to plan and execute.

Table 12-1   Content of an as-planned and as-released baseline for a product.

Table 12-2   Assessment checklist for certifying CMII-compliant tools.

Table 12-3   CMII-compliant software and meaning of certification by ICM.

Table 13-1   Six categories for business process infrastructure assessment.

Table 13-2   Calculation of cost avoidance and cost reduction.

Acronyms

BOM	*Bill of Material (or recipe, or bill of source code files, or bill of anything)*
BOO	*Bill Of Operations (process plan, routing, work instruction)*
CA1	*Change Administration I*
CA2	*Change Administration II*
CA3	*Change Administration III*
CAD	*Computer-Aided Design*
CAE	*Computer-Aided Engineering*
CAGE	*Commercial and/or Government Entity*
CCB	*Configuration Control Board*
CI	*Configuration Item*
CIB	*Change Implementation Board*
CM	*Configuration Management*
CMII	*Configuration Management II*
CRB	*Change Review Board*
DCR	*Document Change Record (or was-is record)*
DID	*Data Item Description*
ECN	*Enterprise Change Notice*
ECP	*Engineering Change Proposal*
ECR	*Enterprise Change Request*
ECO	*Engineering Change Order*
ERP	*Enterprise Requirements Planning*
ICD	*Interface Control Document*
ICM	*Institute of Configuration Management*
ID#	*Identification Number*
ISO	*International Organization for Standardization*
IT	*Information Technology*
JIT	*Just-In-Time*
O&M	*Operation and Maintenance*
O&R	*Overhaul and Repair*
PDM	*Product Data Management*
PLC	*Product Life Cycle*
PR	*Problem Report*
QA	*Quality Assurance*
ROI	*Return-on-Investment*
SPC	*Statistical Process Control*
STEP	*Standard for the Exchange of Product Model Data (international)*
VDD	*Version Description Document*
W/A	*Work Authorization (purchase order, shop order, modification order)*
WBS	*Work Breakdown Structure*

Glossary of Terms

<u>Administrative Hierarchy</u> - hierarchy of policies, management plans, operating standards and supporting procedures which define how an organization runs its business.

<u>Application Requirements</u> - the requirements that an end-item product must achieve in the environment where it is used (such as emission requirements for automobiles).

<u>As-Built Records</u> - completed work authorizations and referenced requirements used to build physical items and to verify their conformance.

<u>As-Planned and As-Released Baseline</u> - contains the entire hierarchy of as-planned and as-released information about an enterprise, a facility or an end-item product. Such a baseline is always current and includes visibility of pending changes and their effectivities.

<u>Bill of Material</u> - defines the parent-to-child relationships between physical items.

<u>Business Process Infrastructure</u> — how the information used to run the business and manage product life cycles is identified, structured, linked and owned, how changes to that information are processed and how the information is kept clear, concise and valid.

<u>Change Implementation Board</u> — a group that plans and implements approved changes.

<u>Change Review Board</u> — a group that reviews change requests and makes business decisions.

<u>Closed-Loop Change Process</u> — a self-correcting process in which any work that enters the process is tracked and guided to satisfactory completion.

<u>Configuration Management and CMII</u> — see page 12 for a traditional definition of CM. See Table 2-2 on page 21 for a refined and combined definition of CM and CMII.

<u>Core Business Processes</u> — within the CMII model for a business enterprise, it is the core processes identified in the strategic business plan and used to achieve all work.

<u>Creator</u> (or author) — each document is co-owned by a creator and a designated user or a team of users. Its creator is the individual who best understands the higher-level requirements.

<u>Culture Problem</u> — the reluctance commonly encountered when users are asked to use a process, procedure or system which is different from what they are accustomed to using.

<u>Decision Tree</u> — structured questions with YES or NO answers that provide a proper decision.

<u>Dependent Demand</u> — the need for an item is driven by the demand for its parent-level item.

<u>Design Basis</u> (or Basis for Detailed Design) — A high-level definition of an end-item which provides a basis for developing detailed designs and processes.

<u>Designated User</u> — an individual who co-owns a document (with its creator) and is responsible for validating that document on behalf of all users.

<u>Effectivity</u> — the timing for when an approved change will be (or was) incorporated into a physical item or process (typically stated by date, lot or serial number).

<u>End-Item</u> — generally refers to "finished items as delivered to customers" or any product or facility as it exists in its finished state.

<u>Enterprise Operating Standards</u> — a consolidated set of the requirements that must be achieved by an organization's core business processes.

<u>Fast-Track Changes</u> — relatively low-risk changes which proceed through the closed-loop change process very quickly and which require the fewest number of approvals.

<u>Indenture Level</u> — a numeric designation of a specific level within an administrative or physical item hierarchy.

<u>Interchangeability</u> — refers to whether or not different items may be used in the same application.

<u>Intervention Resources</u> — resources used to accomplish corrective action and thereby rescue schedules and/or quality.

<u>Item Identification Number</u> — a unique number used to give identity to a specific configuration. Items with the same identification number are expected to be fully interchangeable.

<u>Just-In-Time</u> — the practice of scheduling completions or receipts on a just-in-time basis in which the physical item or document is used immediately.

<u>Life Cycle</u> — the life cycle for a physical item begins with the release of its first definitive document and ends with retirement of its last definitive document.

<u>Life Cycle Phases</u> — could be any number of phases but the five most common include concept, development, production/build, operation/maintenance and decommissioning.

<u>Lot Number</u> — a unique identity which provides the ability to distinguish between different lots of physical items or materials which have the same identification number.

Lowest Common Denominator(s) — the subordinate element or elements within a product or process which represents its most basic and/or common ingredients.

Master Production Schedule — build completion schedule for deliverable end-items.

Model Number — A unique identifier assigned to a like-family of end-items and which are usually serialized. Each model typically has its own as-planned and as-released baseline.

Procedures — documented step-by-step instructions for accomplishing administrative tasks.

Process Plans — documented step-by-step instructions for performing work on physical items.

Producibility — refers to the ability to produce a physical item and achieve its specified design requirements in a manner that is reliable and efficient.

Records — completed authorization forms and referenced documents which provide evidence that required tasks were completed and that the results conformed to requirements.

Reidentification — the assignment of a different identification number to a physical item to signify that the superseding item is no longer interchangeable with the superseded item.

Release — signifies that something has been put into work. For example, documents are released and forms are released.

Release Code — serves to identify the release state of a document.

Significant Number — a physical item identification number in which one or more characters in the number have meaning.

Source Code — code that is written to achieve software design requirements. The code, once written, represents a physical item which is compiled into executable code.

Traceability — end-item versus lot traceability. One traces specific changes to specific end-items, the other traces specific items from their source lot to their current locations.

Version Description Document — a document which references other documents that fully define the latest configuration and the differences between all prior versions.

Where-Used — a listing of all applications of a specific physical item or document.

Work Center — a location or entity which has specialized skills or capabilities for performing specific types of work.

Index

Accommodate change 9,22,55
Administrative hierarchy 67
Administrative procedures 67
Air traffic control system 28
Alcoa 30
Alternate items 84
Application requirements 60
As-planned and as-released baseline 18,
        48,63,69,76,121,124,129
  by model number 57,86-88
  framework 19,58
  tree analogy 63
Arizona Motor Vehicle Division 26

Baseline
  as-planned 18
  as-released 13
  fixed 18
  moving 18,63
Basis for detailed design 100,101
Bills of material 58
  for positive control 80,88
  indenture levels 60,68
  or parts list 58
  planning bills 63,84,92
  structure 57-60
Build-to-order 2,112
Build-to-print 7
Build standards 114
Business enterprise
  administrative hierarchy 67
  business regulations 67
Business of business 48
Business process infrastructure
  baseline as cornerstone 18,22
  formal communications 14

Capacity planning 1,6,117
Change administration I 151
Change administration II 151
Change administration III 151
Change analysis phase 19
Change effectivities 69,76,78
Change faster 10,35,46

Change forms 38,70,74,116
  document change record 38
  enterprise change notice 38,41,70,76
  enterprise change request 38,41
  formats 74
  problem report 38
  work authorization 38
Change impact matrix 76
Change implementation phase 19
Change implementation plan 127
Change implementation roadmap 19
Change life cycle 40
Change management 35,54
Change records 40
Change task tracking 127,150
Classes of objects 38
Clear, concise and valid 9,21,46,47,50-
        52,55
Closed-loop change process 40,69,78,125
CMII
  business process infrastructure 21,47
  certification 128,129,134
  definition 10,21,35,46
  destination 133
  enabling tools 121,123
  implementation steps 131,136 137,144
  model 47,54,55,133,135
  nuggets of wisdom 9
  operating guidelines 24
  organizational alignment 54,148
  principles 108
  process proficiency 137,140
  return-on-investment 139
  training 134,146
  scope 21,46
  skills 151
CMII implementation phases 131
Configuration management
  common tread 23
  from a legal perspective 109
  fundamentals 11
  paradigms 21,22,48
  software 11
  subprocesses 36,54

traditional definition 12
traditional scope 21
reinvented 21,22,54
Communications management 13,22
Concurrent engineering 4,64
Consistent conformance 50,55
Continuous improvement 1,51,55
Core business processes 67,146
Corrective action 1,24,39,51,52,69,140
Corrective action mode 51,91
Cost accounting 20
Cost avoidance 138
Cost reduction 138
Costs by contract 20
Creator 95,126
Critical path 150
Cross-functional team 4,9,134
Customize-to-order 5
Customer order entry 9
Customer order lead time 5
Czerwinski, FF 11

Data integrity 90,91,93,94
Data management 35,42,54
Data migration 94
Data sets used in-series 89,90-92
Delivery systems 48-50,52
Dependent demand 90
Design basis 101-103
Design standards 114
Designated users 95,126
Development 99
   eight-sequenced steps 100
   evolutionary 103,105-7
   milestones 18
   one set of priorities 102
   planned 103
   three tier plan 99,100
   V-Model, 39,99
Deviation 16,75,78
Document
   centric 61
   control 35,44
   costs 82
   effective date 124
   formats 61,68
   identification 70,79
   linkages 59
   number 38,68

owners 8,38
primary 62,68
repositories 40,50,66
release date 63
revision history 63
revision level 38,68,70
revision record 70
secondary 62,68
validation 39
types 38,61,68
Document better 10,35,46

Effective date 124
Effectivity 13,69,124,127
Effectivity maintenance 77
EIA/ANSI-649 12
Employee empowerment 95
Enabling tools 121,128,129,150
End-Item
   application requirements 60
   design basis 101-103
   model 57
Engineering change process 9
Enterprise operating standards 14
Equivalent items 84
ERP systems 92

Functional schematics 101

Glossary of terms 14

Hierarchy
   administrative 67
   physical item 19,58

IBM Federal Systems Division 28
Identification numbers 80,81
   documents 70,80
   physical items 70,80,81
   significant 82
   software programs 87
   source code files 87
Information repositories 66
Information technology 17
Installation drawings 2
Interchangeability 13,69
   by item identification number 20,38,71
   by revision level 71
   rules 71

Interface documents 59,101
Intervention resources 3,53,91
ISO 9000 quality standards 8,49,97

Job shop 111,112
Just-in-time 6,118

Layouts 101
Lead time 1,2
Learning curves 65
Legacy systems 17
Legal liability 109
   role of configuration management 109
   view of documentation 109
   view of producers 109
   view of products 109
   view of workmanship 109
Library management 35,45,54
Life cycle 11,58,68
Lockheed Martin 29,31
Loral 28
Lowest common denominators 38,
      46,61,70

Maquiladora 141
Master production schedule 3
   production plan 3
   master schedule 3
McConnell, Steve 32,108
Measurement 91,119,149
Metadata for documents 125
Metadata for physical items 125
Military standards 11-12
Model number 86
Material requirements planning 1,92

Naming conventions 20,83,86-88
Nonconformances 78
Numbering conventions 20,86-88

Organizational performance 91

Paradigm 6,11,21
Performance measurement 91
Perry, William 12
Philip Crosby 4
Physical Item
   alternates 84
   centric 61

   equivalents 84
   hierarchy 19,57,68
   identification number 38
   interchangeability 20
   primary 62
   secondary 62
   serialization 72,73
   superseded/superseding 63,85,88
   where used 62
Naming conventions 20,79
Nonconformances 16,75
Numbering conventions 20,79

O'Neill, Paul 30
Organizational health 149
Organizational policies 67

Priority control 1
Problem reports 74
Procedures 19
Process assessment 135
Process automation 17
Process maturity `111,119
Process plans 7,101
Product structuring 57,58,68
Project management 35,46,54,115,127
   Shewhart/Deming cycle 36
   dual cycles per CMII 36
Prototypes 2
Purchase orders 38

Quality
   assurance 35,54
   conformance to requirements 15,37,46
   of life 52
   whatever the customer likes 15,37

Random failures 29
Real improvements 138
Records 38,70,84
Records management 35,43,54
Regulated industries 97
Reidentification 71
Release 41,49
Release management 35,41,54
Requirements
   accuracy 90
   clear, concise and valid 9,13,22,50
   do not have to be perfect 96

must be released 49
must lead 16,39,69
netted 90
out-of-control 10
structured 39,57,58
validation 39
Requirements driven 39,47,49
Requirements management 35,39,54
Resource planning 145
Reuse 58,83

Safety 30
Samaras T.T. 11
Secondary documents 62
Secondary items 62
Signatures 8
Software development 33,45,103,105-107
Software development process 33,105
Stand-alone systems 17
Standish Group 25
Stove-pipe processes 17
Suitable for use 16
Supply chain management 6
System schematics 59,101

Terminologies 126
Time to market 58
Titan IV rocket 29
Traceability 69
  end-item 72
  lot 73
Training 134
Transition plan 136,137

U.S. Air Force 16
U.S. Department of Defense 12,42,64
U.S. Federal Aviation Administration 28
U.S. Federal Bureau of Investigation 27
User friendly 121,124

Validation 116
Verification 116

Waiver 75,78
Where used 85
Work authorization 36,38,93
Work centers 111-116

Zero defects 111,126